CHENG & TSUI

"Bringing Asia to the World"™

趣学中文

Go Far
WITH CHINESE

Simplified Characters

Workbook 1

Senior Curriculum Adviser
Ying Jin 金璎

Lead Instructional Contributors

Chunmei Guan 关春梅

Cilei Han 韩慈磊

Zoey Liu 刘喆医

Diane Neubauer 杜雁子

Erica Pollard 狄瑞和

CHENG & TSUI

"Bringing Asia to the World"™

First Edition 2021

28 27 26 25 24   2 3 4 5 6

ISBN 978-1-62291-480-7

Publisher
JILL CHENG

Curriculum Development Manager
MEGAN BURNETT

Curriculum Development Staff
LEI WANG, TAMSIN TRUE-ALCALA,
EMILY PETIT, NING MA, YINGCHUN GUAN

Managing Editor
KAESMENE HARRISON BANKS

Production Coordinator
TODD BROWN

Market and Photo Researchers
MARIAN STACEY, ELIZABETH HANLON

Cover Designers
CHRISTIAN SABOGAL with MARINA LI

Interior Designers
KATE PAPADAKI with MARINA LI

Comic Illustrator
MARGARET LOR

Photographs
© Adobe Stock
© Cheng & Tsui
© Shutterstock

Photo credits are listed on p. viii

Cheng & Tsui Co., Inc.
25 West Street, Boston, MA 02111-1213 USA
P: 617.988.2400 / 800.554.1963
F: 617.426.3669
cheng-tsui.com

Printed in the United States of America

The *Go Far with Chinese* series encompasses textbooks, workbooks, teacher's resources, audio, video, a digital version on Cheng & Tsui FluencyLink™ and more. Visit cheng-tsui.com for more information on the other components of *Go Far with Chinese*.

Contents

Workbook Organization

Each section in the Workbook includes a variety of exercises to help students learn and work with the vocabulary and grammar points introduced in the Textbook. These exercises help students master the Can-Do Goals, which are listed on the first page of each chapter in the Workbook. Each Workbook chapter is divided into four sections that mirror the structure of the Textbook: Section 1, Section 2, Section 3, and Put the Pieces Together.

Sections 1-3

Sections 1-3 of the Workbook are composed of five subsections (in the order listed) that develop different skills: Pinyin and Tone, Listening, Speaking, Reading, and Writing. These subsections are sequenced to allow students to first practice the language aurally and orally, before working with the Chinese characters introduced in the section.

I. Pinyin and Tone

These exercises help students strengthen their understanding of Mandarin Chinese pronunciation. Many exercises include audio support, with some focused on a particularly difficult pinyin sound or tone pattern found in vocabulary words introduced in that section. Other exercises focus on matching the pinyin of vocabulary words to the correct meaning.

II. Listening

Listening passages provide students with valuable language input, both covering new content and reviewing previously-learned material. As students progress through the chapters, these passages and their accompanying comprehension check questions gradually increase in difficulty. The format of the listening exercises, including listening rejoinders, helps students prepare for the types of exercises that they will encounter if they continue their studies and take the AP[1] exam.

III. Speaking

Here, prompts elicit responses in complete Chinese sentences, giving students an opportunity to build interpersonal and presentational speaking proficiency. In some exercises, students are asked to respond to an imagined situation or a specific question; in others, students are asked to describe or comment on a given image.

IV. Reading

Reading passages, including both written dialogues and narratives, provide students with valuable language input and test their comprehension of passages containing section vocabulary. Students build literacy skills as reading passages increase in length and complexity over the course of the Workbook. The Workbook also includes reading exercises based on authentic materials.

V. Writing

These exercises give students the opportunity to use characters to convey meaning. Writing exercises include word scrambles, finish the sentence, and open-ended questions.

[1]AP® is a trademark registered by the College Board, which is not affiliated with, and does not endorse, this product.

Put the Pieces Together!

I. Vocabulary Chart
The Put the Pieces Together! section begins with a vocabulary chart that allows students to track the new words they are expected to know by the end of the chapter. The chart has blank columns for the students to complete by adding in the correct pinyin and definition for each new word learned. To provide an opportunity for personalization, the chart also includes blank rows for students to add the additional words relating to the chapter's topic that are important to them.

II. Reading
This reading is a lengthy dialogue or narrative passage that includes most of the words and grammar points introduced in the chapter. Students answer comprehension questions to check their understanding of the passage.

III. Writing
This writing exercise asks students to describe a situation, create a dialogue, or answer questions according to their own circumstances. Students have an opportunity to write in a creative and unscripted way.

This icon indicates that audio content is available. Audio can be downloaded at cheng-tsui.com.

Meet the Neighbors

The Lopezes are moving to a very international neighborhood in Beijing. In addition to Daming, here are some of their new neighbors. They will appear in dialogues throughout the workbook.

Leo Fischer, 14,
from Germany

Sanjay Patel, 15,
from the United States

Maya Young, 14,
from the United States

Ellen Jones, 16,
from the United Kingdom

Miko Futamura, 16,
from Japan

Owen Kang, 16,
from the United States

Photo Credits

Every effort has been made to accurately credit the copyright owners of materials reproduced in this publication. Omissions brought to our attention will be corrected in subsequent editions.

Chapter 1
p.5, Aaron Amat/Shutterstock.com; Aaron Amat/Shutterstock.com; **p.7,** Luis Molinero/Shutterstock.com; **p.9,** Elena Schweitzer/Shutterstock.com; George Dolgikh/Shutterstock.com; cynoclub/Shutterstock.com; **p.10,** VH-studio/Shutterstock.com

Chapter 2
p.16, coloursinmylife/Shutterstock.com; HelloRF Zcool/Shutterstock.com; **p.17,** photos for composite image by Kindlena/Shutterstock.com and kaer_stock/Shutterstock.com; **p.22,** photos for composite image by Cookie Studio/Shutterstock.com and nakaridore/Shutterstock.com; Crazystone/Shutterstock.com; sasha2109/Shutterstock.com; **p.23,** Kang Sunghee/Shutterstock.com; Ebtikar/Shutterstock.com; Dean Drobot/Shutterstock.com; pixelheadphoto digitalskillset/Shutterstock.com; Rido/Shutterstock.com; ESB Professional/Shutterstock.com; **p.24,** LStockStudio/Shutterstock.com

Chapter 3
p.32, Animashka/Shutterstock.com; **p.33,** Jack Z Young/Shutterstock.com; ESB Professional/Shutterstock.com; **p.35,** Black Rock Digital/Shutterstock.com; **p.39,** Mangostar/Shutterstock.com; Mark Deibert Productions/Shutterstock.com; Chupryna S./Shutterstock.com; Sam Wordley/Shutterstock.com; **p.40,** Xeniya Butenko/Shutterstock.com; Ammit Jack/Shutterstock.com; photomaster/Shutterstock.com; **p.41,** Happy monkey/Shutterstock.com; Piotr Wawrzyniuk/Shutterstock.com

Chapter 4
p.49, Lucky Business/Shutterstock.com; **p.50,** Tarzhanova/Shutterstock.com; **p.52,** Monkey Business Images/Shutterstock.com; **p.53,** PR Image Factory/Shutterstock.com; **p.57,** Mas Ud/Shutterstock.com; Vector Stall/Shutterstock.com

Chapter 5
p.64, Great_Kit/Shutterstock.com; Great_Kit/Shutterstock.com; Great_Kit/Shutterstock.com; Great_Kit/Shutterstock.com; **p.65,** Master1305/Shutterstock.com; **p.67,** Sergei Ryzhov/Shutterstock.com; arek_malang/Shutterstock.com; Monkey Business Images/Shutterstock.com; Master1305/Shutterstock.com; **p.70,** Zerbor/Shutterstock.com; maximmmmum/Shutterstock.com; Chikovnaya/Shutterstock.com; Ilya Bolotov/Shutterstock.com; **p.72,** Vector Stall/Shutterstock.com; Rvector/Shutterstock.com; Mas Ud/Shutterstock.com; Gerrie FIrdaus/Shutterstock.com; Rvector/Shutterstock.com; Mas Ud/Shutterstock.com; Gerrie FIrdaus/Shutterstock.com; Bluekat/Shutterstock.com; Mas Ud/Shutterstock.com; **p.73,** Kostov/Shutterstock.com; pr2is/Shutterstock.com; moxumbic/Shutterstock.com; **p.74,** baldyrgan/Shutterstock.com; **p.75,** Great_Kit/Shutterstock.com; Oleh Markov/Shutterstock.com

Chapter 6
p.80, TheHighestQualityImages/Shutterstock.com; photos for composite image by M.E. Mulder/Shutterstock.com and AGCuesta/Shutterstock.com; CapturePB/Shutterstock.com; photos for composite image by lem/Shutterstock.com, Peter Voronov/Shutterstock.com, and Svitlana Varfolomieieva/Shutterstock.com; **p.81,** Chinaview/Shutterstock.com; TheHighestQualityImages/Shutterstock.com; M.E. Mulder/Shutterstock.com; Svitlana Varfolomieieva/Shutterstock.com; **p.85,** photos for composite image by M.E. Mulder/Shutterstock.com, Cookie Studio/Shutterstock.com, and TheHighestQualityImages/Shutterstock.com; **p.88,** Iakov Filimonov/Shutterstock.com; Dragon Images/Shutterstock.com; **p.90,** photos for composite image by Panupat99/Shutterstock.com, linlypu/Shutterstock.com, elwynn/Shutterstock.com, and linlypu/Shutterstock.com

Chapter 7
p.99, PINK_SUWANNA/Shutterstock.com; **p.102,** Featureflash Photo Agency/Shutterstock.com; zhangjin_net/Shutterstock.com; Robert Foothorap; **p.103,** photos for composite image Vitya_M/Shutterstock.com and Vasilius/Shutterstock.com; **p.106,** icons for composit image by Viktoria Kurpas/Shutterstock.com; **p.108,** XiXinXing/Shutterstock.com

Getting to Know Chinese

Can-Do Goals

In this chapter, you have learned about:

- Different Chinese dialects

- Chinese characters

- Pinyin, a system to sound out Chinese characters

- The structure of simple Chinese sentences

In this chapter, you are also learning to:

- Greet someone in Chinese

- Create simple sentences in Chinese

- Understand some words and phrases for the classroom

- Write the numbers one through ten in Chinese characters

Introduction to Chinese

Fill out the KWL chart below in English about what you know, what you want to know, and what you have learned about the Chinese language. There are no right or wrong answers. Just write whatever you can for each column.

K	W	L
What I **K**now:	What I **W**ant to Know:	What I Have Learned:

Mandarin pronunciation

A. Write the letters of the following words next to the parts of the pinyin word they describe.

(a) tone   **(b)** initial   **(c)** final

B. Circle the pinyin word that is second tone. Underline the pinyin word that is third tone.

1. bǎ   **2.** bà   **3.** bā   **4.** bá

Audio

C. Listen to the recording and repeat each pinyin word that you hear. Try your best to imitate the tones.

Audio

	First tone	Second tone	Third tone	Fourth tone
1.	bā	bá	bǎ	bà
2.	dā	dá	dǎ	dà
3.	mā	má	mǎ	mà
4.	nā	ná	nǎ	nà

D. Match each description to the pinyin word it describes.

1. The word has the initial "sh," the final "i," and the fourth tone mark.   **a.** shī

2. The word has the initial "m," the final "ei," and the second tone mark.   **b.** shì

3. The word has the initial "m," the final "ei," and the third tone mark.   **c.** méi

4. The word has the initial "sh," the final "i," and the first tone mark.   **d.** měi

Getting started in Chinese

A. Write the letters of the following grammar terms above the parts of the pinyin sentence they describe.

(a) object   **(b)** subject   **(c)** verb

(   )   (   )   (   )

Wǒ   xǐhuan   tā.

I   like   it.   →   I like it.

B. Circle the word you add at the end of a sentence to ask a simple yes/no question. Underline the word you add before a verb to answer "no" to a question.

1. bù   **2.** nǐ   **3.** tā   **4.** ma

C. Turn the following sentences into questions.

1. Nǐ xǐhuan tā. (You like it.)

   Change to: Do you like it? _____?

2. Nǐ xǐhuan gǒu. (You like dogs.)

   Change to: Do you like dogs? _____?

3. Nǐ xǐhuan māo. (You like cats.)

   Change to: Do you like cats? _____?

D. Answer the following question. First give a "yes" answer, then a "no" answer.

Nǐ **xǐhuan** tā ma? (Do you like it?)

"Yes" answer:

1. _____

"No" answer:

2. _____

E. Listen to the dialogue and mark the following statements true (T) or false (F).

🔊 Audio

	T	F
1. The man is asking a question.	○	○
2. The woman answers "yes" to the question.	○	○
3. The woman asks a question at the end.	○	○

Useful phrases for the classroom

A. Count the number of the third tones and the number of the "-ao" finals in each phrase. Then listen to the recording, paying close attention to how each word is pronounced.

	The number of third-tones	The number of "-ao" finals
1. Nǐ hǎo! (Hello!)		
2. Lǎoshī hǎo! (Hello, teacher!)		
3. Wǒ bù zhīdào. (I don't know.)		

B. Listen to the recording of the words below. Then answer the questions that follow.

Xièxie! (Thank you!)

Duìbuqǐ! (I'm sorry!; Excuse me!)

Méi guānxi! (It's nothing!; That's all right!)

Zàijiàn! (Goodbye!)

Qǐng jǔ shǒu. (Please raise your hand.)

Qǐng zuò. (Please sit.)

	Yes	No
1. Does the "x" sound in Mandarin sound the same as the "x" sound in English?	○	○
2. Does the "q" sound in Mandarin sound the same as the "q" sound in English?	○	○
3. Does the "d" sound in Mandarin sound the same as the "d" sound in English?	○	○
4. Does the "b" sound in Mandarin sound the same as the "b" sound in English?	○	○
5. Does the "z" sound in Mandarin sound the same as the "z" sound in English?	○	○

C. Listen to the three phrases, and match them to the correct pinyin.

Audio

Phrase 1	**a.** Wǒ bù zhīdào. (I don't know.)
Phrase 2	**b.** Zhōngwén (the Chinese language)
Phrase 3	**c.** Qǐng zhàn qǐlái. (Please stand up.)

D. Listen to the recording and put a check next to the number of each phrase in which a request is made with **qǐng**.

Audio

1. _____   2. _____   3. _____   4. _____

E. Listen to the recording and put a check next to the number of each dialogue in which the man gives a "yes" answer to the woman's question.

Audio

1. _____   2. _____   3. _____   4. _____

F. What are three phrases that you think will be important for you to know how to say? Practice saying them in Chinese.

G. What are two phrases that you think you will hear often and need to understand? Practice saying them in Chinese.

Writing characters is as easy as one, two, three...

A. Look closely at the following characters and how they are written. Write down the number of strokes in each character and give the meaning.

1.   Meaning: _____

   Number of strokes: ____

2.   Meaning: _____

   Number of strokes: _____

3.   Meaning: _____

   Number of strokes: _____

4.   Meaning: _____

   Number of strokes: _____

B. Write the answers to these math questions in Chinese characters.

1. 七 + 三 = _____

2. 四 – 三 = _____

3. 六 + 二 = _____

C. Listen to the recording of the following access code and draw lines to match each Arabic numeral to the correct pinyin above, and to the correct Chinese character below.

yī èr sān sì wǔ liù qī bā jiǔ

3 5 4 - 6 7 1 - 8 9 2

一　二　三　四　五　六　七　八　九

D. Count the number of objects in each image below and write the answer for each image in Arabic numeral, pinyin, and Chinese character.

Flowers	Eggs	Kittens
Arabic numeral: ___	Arabic numeral: ___	Arabic numeral: ___
Pinyin: _____	Pinyin: _____	Pinyin: _____
Chinese character: _____	Chinese character: _____	Chinese character: _____

Writing more complex characters and sentences

A. Listen as each word is read and match it to the correct pinyin.

1. 老师   2. 学生   3. 我   4. 是   5. 吗   6. 不

(a) lǎoshī   **(b)** xuéshēng   **(c)** bù   **(d)** wǒ   **(e)** ma   **(f)** shì

B. It's Teacher's Day! Use a Mandarin phrase to greet your teacher.

C. Read the dialogue and mark the statements that follow true (T) or false (F).

Man: 你好，你是老师吗？

Woman: 是，我是老师。你是学生吗？

Man: 是。老师好！

Woman: 你好！

Man: 老师，再见！

Woman: 再见！

	T	F
1. The woman is a student.	○	○
2. The man is a student.	○	○
3. The man says goodbye to the woman at the end of the conversation.	○	○

D. Match the type of composition to the character by writing the appropriate letter in the blank next to each character. (Note: you will use some letters more than once.)

(a) left-right character   **(b)** top-bottom character   **(c)** enclosing character

1. 好 __   2. 学 __   3. 国 __   4. 师 __   5. 是 __

Put the Pieces Together!

1 Chapter Vocabulary Chart

Fill in the pinyin of and the definition for each word that you learned in this chapter. Use the extra spaces at the bottom of the chart to add any additional words you learned.

No.	Word	Pinyin	Definition
1	你好		
2	你		
3	好		
4	是		
5	老师		
6	吗		
7	我		
8	不		
9	学生		
10	再见		
11	一		

No.	Word	Pinyin	Definition
12	二		
13	三		
14	四		
15	五		
16	六		
17	七		
18	八		
19	九		
20	十		

II Reading

A. Connect a character from Column A to a character from Column B to create a word.

Column A

1. 你
2. 老
3. 学
4. 再

Column B

a. 好
b. 生
c. 见
d. 师

III Writing

A. Rearrange the Chinese words to translate the English sentences.

1. Are you a teacher?

_____

是 ┊ 吗？ ┊ 你 ┊ 老师

2. I am a student.

_____

学生。 ┊ 我 ┊ 是

3. I am not a teacher.

_____

不 ┊ 我 ┊ 老师。 ┊ 是

What's in a Name?

Can-Do Goals

In this chapter, you are learning to:

- Understand how Chinese names are different from English names

- Tell others your name

- Ask for someone's name

- Say that something belongs to someone

- Respond to "what" and "who" questions

- Express that you have or do not have something

Exchanging names

Audio

I   Pinyin and Tone

A. The sh- initial is a common sound in Chinese. It is the sound at the beginning of 什么. Listen to the following words and circle all those that have the sh- initial sound.

1. 是   2. 三   3. 四   4. 生   5. 师

B. Listen to the tone of each character you hear. Write a 1 next to the words that are first tone.

1. zhong _____   2. wen _____   3. ba _____   4. ying _____   5. jiao _____

Audio

II   Listening

A. You will hear three brief self-introductions. Write the letter of the image that matches each self-introduction you hear.

1. _____

2. _____

3. _____

B. Listen to the self-introduction, then mark the letter of the option that best completes each statement.

1. The speaker mentioned
   (a) his Chinese name and his English name.
   (b) only his English name.

2. The speaker's surname is
   (a) Bái.
   (b) Míng.

3. The speaker is
   (a) a student and a teacher.
   (b) a teacher only.

4. The speaker teaches
   (a) English.
   (b) Chinese.

III Speaking

A. Imagine a new student is joining your Chinese class. Introduce yourself and give your English name and your Chinese name, if you have one.

IV Reading

A. Take a look at this name tag for a new student in a Chinese class. Besides the student's name, the name tag also lists the name of the course and the instructor. What is the teacher's name?

名字：Aria Clarke

中文（一）
老师：白英

你好！中文

Teacher's name: _____

B. Create a logical dialogue by filling in each blank with the letter of the appropriate sentence that follows.

 你叫什么名字？

 1. _____

 你的英文名字是什么？

 2. _____

 3. _____

 我叫 Leo。

(a) 我的英文名字是 Owen。

(b) 我叫大文。

(c) 你叫什么名字？

V Writing

A. Use the words in the list to complete the sentences. You will use each word only once.

Choices: 什么，中文，的，名字

1. 他是我 _____ 老师。

2. 我的中文 _____ 是大明。

3. 你有 _____ 名字吗？

4. 你的英文名字是 _____ ?

B. Rearrange the Chinese words to translate the English sentences.

1. What is your name? (What name are you called?)

什么 ┊ 名字？ ┊ 你 ┊ 叫

2. What is your Chinese name?

什么？ ┊ 你的 ┊ 名字 ┊ 中文 ┊ 是

3. My English name is Dan.

英文 ┊ 是 Dan。 ┊ 名字 ┊ 我的

4. My name is Bái Dàmíng. (I am called Bái Dàmíng.)

白 ┊ 叫 ┊ 大明。 ┊ 我

Saying that you have (or don't have) something

Audio

I Pinyin and Tone

A. Listen to the recording and fill in final sounds you hear. You do not need to mark the tone.

1. sh _____   2. x _____   3. y _____   4. m _____

B. The Lopezes' Chinese surname is 林, which is a second tone word. Listen to the following common surnames and write a 2 next to the surnames that are second tone.

1. Zhang _____   2. Wang _____   3. Chen _____   4. Liu _____

Audio

II Listening

A. Listen to the dialogue, then circle the letter of the option that best completes each statement.

1. The girl is the boy's
   (a) classmate.
   (b) sister.
   (c) neither.

2. The girl's Chinese name is
   (a) Mǎ Yuèyue.
   (b) Dīng Báilín.
   (c) tóngxué.

B. Listen to the dialogue and mark the following statements true (T) or false (F).

	T	F
1. Isabella has a Chinese teacher.	○	○
2. Isabella's Chinese teacher is Bái Dàmíng.	○	○
3. It is likely that they both already know Bái Dàmíng.	○	○

III Speaking

A. Use complete Chinese sentences to introduce these three people.

IV Reading

A. Draw a line to the statement that best answers each question.

1. 她是谁？

2. 他是谁？

3. 她有中文名字吗？

4. 他叫什么名字？

(a) 他是我的同学。

(b) 她是我的老师。

(c) 她有中文名字。

(d) 他叫明明。

B. Read the dialogue and mark the statements that follow true (T) or false (F).

 她是谁？

 她是我的同学。

 她叫什么名字？

 她叫英英。

 英英是她的英文名字吗？

 英英是她的中文名字。

	T	F
1. Maya and Leo are talking about a boy.	○	○
2. The person Maya and Leo are talking about is Maya's classmate.	○	○
3. Maya tells Leo the person's Chinese name.	○	○

V Writing

A. Complete the caption of each photo by adding 我 , 你 , or 她 . Use each word only once.

_____ 是谁?　　　_____ 是谁?　　　_____ 是谁?

B. Complete the translation of each sentence.

 她是 _____?

Who is she?

 _____ 是我的同学。她 _____ 白文文。

She is my classmate. Her name is Wenwen Bai.

 她 _____ 英文 _____ 吗?

Does she have an English name?

 她 _____ 英文名字。

She doesn't have an English name.

Introducing more than one person

I Pinyin and Tone

Audio

A. 和 is a second tone character and 也 is a third tone character. Listen to the tone of each character you hear. Write a 2 next to the characters that are second tone. Write a 3 next to the characters that are third tone.

1. 同 ___ 2. 有 ___ 3. 林 ___ 4. 明 ___ 5. 你 ___ 6. 马 ___

II Listening

Audio

A. Listen to the dialogues and select the picture that best matches the topic of each conversation.

1.

2.

III Speaking

A. Choose one teacher at your school and name all the students in your Chinese class who have that teacher. Answer orally in a complete Chinese sentence.

B. Look at the photo and explain in Chinese whether the people shown are teachers or students, and whether or not they are classmates.

IV Reading

A. Two friends are looking at a photo in a school yearbook. Read their conversation and mark the statements that follow true (T) or false (F).

Girl: 她们是老师吗？

Boy: 她们不是老师。她们是学生。

Girl: 他们也是学生吗？

Boy: 他们也是学生。她们和他们是同学。

	T	F
1. Some of the people in the photo are teachers.	○	○
2. There are both boys and girls in the picture.	○	○
3. The students in the picture are not classmates.	○	○

B. Read the description of who is shown in this image, then circle the letter of the option that best completes each statement.

我叫 Isabella Lopez。我的中文名字是林春月。她叫 Aria，他叫 Matt。我和他们是同学，也是朋友。

1. The writer has
   (a) an English name.
   (b) a Chinese name.
   (c) both an English name and a Chinese name.

2. Aria and Matt are the writer's
   (a) friends.
   (b) classmates.
   (c) friends and classmates.

A. Complete the sentences below by adding either 和 or 也 . You will use each word twice.

1. 她们是我的朋友。她们 ＿＿＿ 是我的同学。

2. 你 ＿＿＿ 他是朋友吗？

3. 我们和他们是同学。我们 ＿＿＿ 她们 ＿＿＿ 是同学。

B. Complete the translation of each sentence.

1. We are good friends.

我们是好 ＿＿＿＿＿。

2. They are our classmates.

他们是 ＿＿＿＿＿ 的同学。

3. Are you all also students?

＿＿＿＿＿ 也是学生吗？

Put the Pieces Together!

I Chapter Vocabulary Chart

Fill in the pinyin for and the definition of each word that you learned in this chapter. Use the extra spaces at the end of the chart to add any additional words you learned.

No.	Word	Pinyin	Definition
1	叫		
2	什么		
3	名字		
4	的		
5	英文		
6	中文		
7	她		
8	谁		
9	同学		
10	有		
11	没有		

No.	Word	Pinyin	Definition
12	他		
13	他们		
14	和		
15	她们		
16	也		
17	你们		
18	我们		
19	朋友		
20			
21			
22			
23			
24			
25			

II Reading

A. Read the following conversation between Daming, Martin, and Isabella and then answer the questions that follow.

白大明是马丁和春月的中文老师，也是他们的朋友。

 马丁、春月，你们好！

 大明，你好！

 你们有中文名字，你们的同学
也有中文名字吗？

 我的同学没有中文名字。

 我的同学也没有中文名字。

1. Daming is Martin and Isabella's
   (a) friend and Chinese teacher.
   (b) friend only.
   (c) Chinese teacher only.

2. Daming asks Martin and Isabella
   (a) what their Chinese names are.
   (b) if they like learning Chinese.
   (c) if their classmates have Chinese names.

3. How many of Martin's classmates have Chinese names?
   (a) none
   (b) one
   (c) all of them

A. In this chapter you've learned how to introduce yourself and others. On the lines below, write a few sentences introducing yourself and one of your classmates, including your English names and your Chinese names, if you have them. As you write, try to use at least two of the three elements listed below.

我叫⋯⋯

我的同学⋯⋯

她 / 他的中文名字是⋯⋯

_____

_____

_____

_____

_____

Tell Me About Yourself

Can-Do Goals   In this chapter, you are learning to:

- Understand simple descriptions of families

- Ask and answer questions about family members

- Express how many siblings and pets you have

- Understand when others talk about their likes and dislikes

- Talk about likes and dislikes

- Use different measure words to talk about people and animals

Talking about siblings

I Pinyin and Tone

Audio

A. Listen to the recording and number the pinyin in the order the words are spoken. Then draw a line from each pinyin word to the illustration that matches its meaning.

____ gēge   ____ dìdi   ____ māma   ____ mèimei   ____ bàba   ____ jiějie

B. Listen to the tone of each character you hear. Write a 3 next to the characters that are third tone. Write a 1 next to the characters that are first tone.

1. 姐 ___   2. 有 ___   3. 哥 ___   4. 妈 ___   5. 老 ___   6. 师 ___

II Listening

A. Listen to the dialogue and mark the following statements true (T) or false (F).

	T	F
1. The man has an older brother.	◯	◯
2. The man is an older brother.	◯	◯
3. The man doesn't have a younger sister.	◯	◯
4. The man has one younger brother.	◯	◯

B. Listen to each question, then listen to the three possible answers. Mark the letter of the statement that best answers each question.

1. (a) (b) (c)
2. (a) (b) (c)
3. (a) (b) (c)

C. Listen to the girl and the boy describe their families, then list their family members in pinyin beside their pictures.

1. _____

2. _____

III Speaking

A. Find a photo of a family — it can be your family or the family of someone you admire — and talk about who is in the family.

IV Reading

A. Fill in the blanks with the letter of the word that best completes each sentence. Use each word only once.

(a) 一   (b) 几   (c) 个   (d) 没

1. 你有几 __ 哥哥？
2. 我有 __ 个哥哥。
3. 你有 __ 个姐姐？
4. 我 __ 有姐姐。

B. One of the students in Martin's Chinese class is asking him about his siblings. Create a logical dialogue by filling in each blank with the letter of one of the sentences that follow.

Girl: 马丁，你是不是哥哥？

Martin: 1.__ 我是弟弟。

Girl: 2.__

Martin: 有！ 3.__ 你也有姐姐吗？

Girl: 4.__

(a) 我不是哥哥。
(b) 我有一个姐姐！
(c) 我没有姐姐 。
(d) 你有没有姐姐？

Ⓥ Writing

A. Read each question, then use the words below the answer line to write a meaningful answer.

1. **Q:** 马丁有没有姐姐？

   A: _____

   姐姐。｜有｜马丁

2. **Q:** 马丁是不是妹妹？

   A: _____

   是｜妹妹。｜马丁｜不

3. **Q:** 春月有两个弟弟吗？

   A: _____

   春月｜一个｜没有，｜有｜弟弟。

B. Answer the question below in Chinese characters based on the photo.

Q: 她是姐姐吗？

A: _____

_____

_____

Expressing likes and dislikes

Audio

I Pinyin and Tone

A. Listen to the recording carefully. You will hear the word 电视, which has a fourth tone–fourth tone pattern. You will then hear four more words. Put a check next to the number for each word that has the fourth tone–fourth tone pattern.

1. _____   2. _____   3. _____   4. _____

Audio

II Listening

A. Listen to the dialogue and answer the questions that follow.

1. Which of these statements is true?
   (a) The man has an older brother and the woman has an older sister.
   (b) The man has an older sister and the woman has an older brother.
   (c) The man and the woman both have older brothers.
   (d) Neither the man nor the woman has an older brother.

2. According to the dialogue, who likes to read?
   (a) The man, the woman, and both of their older siblings like to read.
   (b) Only the woman likes to read.
   (c) Only the man's older sister likes to read.
   (d) The man's older sister and the woman like to read.

3. According to the dialogue, who likes to watch TV?
   (a) The man, the woman, and both their older siblings like to watch TV.
   (b) Only the woman's older brother likes to watch TV.
   (c) The woman and her older brother like to watch TV.
   (d) It's not mentioned.

B. Listen to each question, then listen to the three possible answers. Mark the letter of the statement that best answers the question.

1. ⓐ   ⓑ   ⓒ

2. ⓐ   ⓑ   ⓒ

C. Listen to the passage and answer the following questions.

   1. What is the speaker's name?
     (a) Her name is Jiàowén.
     (b) Her name is Chūnyuè.
     (c) Her name is Wénwen.

   2. What does the speaker's mother do for work?
     (a) She is a Chinese teacher.
     (b) She is an English teacher.
     (c) She is a teacher, but the speaker doesn't say what she teaches.

   3. How many siblings does the speaker have?
     (a) The speaker has two siblings — an older brother and an older sister.
     (b) The speaker has three siblings — an older brother and two older sisters.
     (c) The speaker has four siblings — an older brother and sister, and a younger brother and sister.

III Speaking

A. Imagine that you are introducing your friend Mark to a Chinese exchange student at your school. Based on the information below, introduce Mark in Chinese.

- Mark has two younger sisters.
- Mark likes to read and watch TV.

B. Look at this picture of a family relaxing in their living room. What does everyone seem to like and not like to do?

IV Reading

A. Take a look at this Chinese poster. Here, the character 少 (shǎo) means that you should do something less and 多 (duō) means you should do something more. What is this poster advising you to do?

少看电视多看书

Answer: _____

B. Read the passage and mark the circles below to show what the people in the family like to do. Mark all that apply.

我很喜欢看电视，可是我的弟弟不喜欢看电视。
我的妈妈很喜欢看书，爸爸也很喜欢看书，可是
弟弟不太喜欢看书。我也不喜欢看书。

	Me	Younger Brother	Mom	Dad
1. Likes watching TV	○	○	○	○
2. Likes reading	○	○	○	○

V Writing

A. Look at the photos and write the one phrase below that describes how each person feels. Use each phrase only once.

Phrases: 很喜欢， 喜欢， 不太喜欢， 不喜欢

How does the woman feel about milk and cookies?

How does the girl feel about what she is watching?

How does the girl feel about the rabbit?

How does the girl feel about broccoli?

1. _____ 2. _____ 3. _____ 4. _____

B. Read each answer, then rearrange the words that follow to create a logical question.

1. A: 我不太喜欢看书。

 Q: _____

 看书？ 喜欢 你 喜欢 不

2. A: 我们也喜欢看书。

 Q: _____

 看书 看书。 她 你们 喜欢 吗？ 喜欢

3. A: 我的姐姐喜欢看电视，可是我的弟弟不喜欢看电视。

 Q: _____

 不 看电视？ 喜欢 姐姐 喜欢 弟弟 和 你的

Talking about pets

Audio

I Pinyin and Tone

A. Circle all the characters that have the "sh" sound. Underline all the characters that have the "x" sound.

1. 是   2. 喜   3. 小   4. 学   5. 书   6. 视

Audio

II Listening

A. Listen to the dialogue and mark the following statements true (T) or false (F).

	T	F
1. The man really likes dogs.	○	○
2. The woman has three dogs.	○	○
3. The man has no dogs.	○	○

B. You will hear three people describe how many pets they have. Write the letter of the image that matches each description you hear.

1. _____

2. _____

3. _____

III Speaking

A. In Chinese, talk about whether or not you like pets and how many you have.

B. In Chinese, give a brief description of each photo.

IV Reading

A. Can you tell what each of the three stores sells? Draw a line between the store sign and the English word for what it sells.

好朋友宠物会馆

云电视

旧书新生

1   2   3

TVs   Books   Pets

B. Read the dialogue and mark the statements that follow true (T) or false (F).

Girl: 你们有宠物吗？

Boy: 有。

Girl: 你们有几只宠物？

Boy: 我们有四只宠物。

Girl: 四只宠物！你很喜欢宠物吗？

Boy: 我不太喜欢宠物，可是我的爸爸、
妈妈、姐姐和弟弟很喜欢宠物。

	T	F
1. The boy likes pets.	○	○
2. The boy has four pets.	○	○
3. The boy's older sister likes pets.	○	○

V Writing

A. Read the sentences below. If a measure word is needed, write in the correct one.

1. 我有三 ___ 妹妹。
2. 他没有 ___ 哥哥。
3. 我们有两 ___ 宠物。
4. 他们有 ___ 宠物。
5. 她有两 ___ 弟弟。

B. Rearrange the Chinese words to translate the English sentences.

1. My older brother has one pet.

_____

| 只 | 有 | 哥哥 | 一 | 我的 | 宠物。 |

2. My older sister also has one pet.

_____

| 姐姐 | 有 | 我的 | 只 | 一 | 宠物。 | 也 |

3. We have two pets, but I don't like pets!

_____

| 两 | 宠物， | 宠物！ | 不 | 只 | 喜欢 | 可是 |
| 我 | 有 | 我们 |

Put the Pieces Together!

▌ Chapter Vocabulary Chart

Fill in the pinyin for and the definition of each word that you learned in this chapter. Use the extra spaces at the end of the chart to add any additional words you learned.

No.	Word	Pinyin	Definition
1	哥哥		
2	姐姐		
3	几		
4	个		
5	弟弟		
6	妹妹		
7	爸爸		
8	妈妈		
9	喜欢		
10	看		
11	书		

No.	Word	Pinyin	Definition
12	很		
13	电视		
14	不太		
15	可是		
16	宠物		
17	只		
18	它		
19	猫		
20	狗		
21	两		

A. Read the passage and answer the questions.

我和春月是同学。我的爸爸和春月的妈妈也是
同学。我有一个妹妹，春月有一个弟弟。他们
不是同学，可是他们是朋友。我的妹妹很喜欢
宠物，春月的弟弟也喜欢宠物。我的妹妹喜欢
看电视，可是春月的弟弟不喜欢看电视。

1. Which of the following statements is correct?
  (a) The writer has a brother.
  (b) Isabella's brother and the writer's sister are not friends.
  (c) Both the writer's sister and Isabella's brother like pets.
  (d) The writer's sister doesn't like watching TV.

2. Match the people who are classmates by drawing lines between them.

  1. the writer   a. Isabella's mother

  2. the writer's sister   b. Isabella

  3. the writer's father   c. Isabella's brother

III Writing

A. In this chapter, you had a chance to ask your classmates a lot of questions! Write a list of three to five things that you learned about them.

_____

_____

_____

_____

_____

Goodbye America, Hello China!

Can-Do Goals   In this chapter, you are learning to:

- Describe something that two or more people have in common

- Understand where someone is and say where you are

- Ask someone to make a choice between two options

- Use "this" and "that" to refer to things if you do not know the words in Chinese

- Talk about your location now and your location this week

Talking about groups

I   Pinyin and Tone

Audio

A. Listen as the words below are read. Circle the words that have the same tone as 学.

1. 人   2. 都   3. 国   4. 对

II   Listening

Audio

A. Listen to the dialogue and mark the following statements true (T) or false (F).

	T	F
1. All three speakers are American.	○	○
2. Both girls like learning Chinese.	○	○
3. The boy also likes learning Chinese.	○	○

B. Listen to the speaker talk about her classmates. Then mark the following statements true (T) or false (F).

	T	F
1. The speaker and her classmates are all Chinese.	○	○
2. The speaker and her classmates all like reading.	○	○
3. The speaker and her classmates all like reading Chinese books.	○	○

III   Speaking

A. Try to think of at least three things you have in common with other students in your Chinese class. Use 都 to talk about these things in complete Chinese sentences.

B. Imagine that the students in the following image are your classmates. Describe the students in Chinese and invent details about individuals in the group and the group as a whole. Use 都 at least once.

Reading

A. Fill in the blanks with the letter of the word that best completes each sentence. Use each word only once.

(a) 学   (b) 都   (c) 美国

1. 林春月和林马丁都是 ＿ 人。

2. 他们 ＿ 喜欢学中文。

3. 马大文喜欢 ＿ 英文。

B. Read the passage and mark the statements that follow true (T) or false (F).

月月、欢欢和文文都是我的同学。她们都有一个妹妹。她们都没有宠物。她们都不喜欢看电视。她们都是我的好朋友。我很喜欢她们！

	T	F
1. All three of the girls are the writer's classmates.	○	○
2. All three of the girls have two younger sisters.	○	○
3. None of the girls have pets.	○	○
4. Some of the girls like to watch TV.	○	○
5. All of the girls are good friends with the writer.	○	○

C. _re checking your shirt's tag to see where it was manufactured. With the help of the ch_ cters you know, can you guess what the last line in Chinese says?

V Writing

A. Use the words in the list to complete the translation of the sentences. You will use some words more than once.

Choices: 都，有，不，中文，弟弟，喜欢，学

1. 你们_____ _____学中文吗？

   Do you all like learning Chinese?

2. 我们 _____ 喜欢 _____ _____。

   We all like learning Chinese.

3. 我们 _____ _____ 哥哥。

   Both of us have older brothers.

4. 我们 _____ 是 _____。

   Both of us are younger brothers.

5. 我们 _____ _____ _____看电视。

   None of us like watching TV.

B. Use complete Chinese sentences to answer the following questions about you and your best friend.

1. 你们都是中国人吗？

   _____

2. 你们都有宠物吗？

   _____

3. 你们都有哥哥吗？

   _____

4. 你们都学中文吗？

   _____

Using 还是 to ask questions

Audio

I Pinyin and Tone

A. Listen to the recording, paying special attention to the initial sounds you hear. Put a check next to the number of each word that starts with the zh- initial sound.

1. _____   2. _____   3. _____   4. _____   5. _____

Audio

II Listening

A. Three friends are looking at this yearbook photo. Listen to their conversation, then choose the option that correctly completes each sentence.

1. The three friends are talking about
   (a) their classmate.
   (b) the boy's friend.
   (c) a teacher.

2. The person they are talking about
   (a) is from Beijing.
   (b) is from China, but not from Beijing.
   (c) isn't Chinese.

B. Listen to each question, then listen to the three possible answers. Mark the letter of the statement that best answers each question.

1. (a) (b) (c)

2. (a) (b) (c)

3. (a) (b) (c)

C. Two classmates are looking at a photo and talking about their siblings. Listen to their conversation and choose the option that correctly completes each sentence.

1. The girl is one of
   (a) two siblings — she has an older brother.
   (b) two siblings — she has a younger brother.
   (c) three siblings — she has an older brother and a younger brother.

2. The boy is
   (a) an older brother.
   (b) a younger brother.
   (c) a middle child.

3. The boy's older siblings
   (a) are not students.
   (b) both study Chinese.
   (c) might be twins.

III Speaking

A. Examine the picture below and think of a question you could ask one of the people in the picture. Try to include the word 还是 in your question.

IV Reading

A. Fill in the blanks with the letter of the word that best completes the sentence. Use each word only once.

(a) 叫   (b) 这   (c) 北京   (d) 是

＿＿个人是我的朋友，她＿＿林春月。她＿＿美国人。那个人也是我的朋友。她是＿＿人。

B. Read the dialogue and then mark the following statements true (T) or false (F).

Mingming: 那个人是谁？你知道吗？

Wenwen: 知道。她是我的同学。

Mingming: 她是中国人还是美国人？

Wenwen: 她是中国人。

Mingming: 她是北京人吗？

Wenwen: 她是北京人。

	T	F
1. The person Mingming and Wenwen are talking about is Wenwen's classmate.	○	○
2. The person Mingming and Wenwen are talking about is American.	○	○
3. The person Mingming and Wenwen are talking about is from Beijing.	○	○
4. Mingming has probably never met the person he and Wenwen are talking about.	○	○

V Writing

A. Use the words in the list to complete the dialogue.

Choices: 喜欢，还是，我，这个，那个

  你喜欢 _____ _____ _____？

她是 _____ _____ 那个。

B. Complete the translations below.

1. Do you like this one or that one?

你喜欢这个 _____？

2. Is he American or Chinese?

他是美国人 _____？

3. Do you all study Chinese or English?

你们都学中文 _____？

4. Is she your older sister or your younger sister?

她是你的姐姐 _____？

Asking about locations

Audio

I Pinyin and Tone

A. Look at the partial pinyin words written below and listen to the recording. For each word you hear that starts with the x- initial sound, complete the pinyin by writing in the x.

1. ____ué   2. ____iǎo   3. ____ài   4. ____īng   5. ____iàn

B. Listen to the recording carefully. You will hear the word 小区, in which the syllable 区 ends with the -ü sound. (Reminder: the -ü sound is written simply as -u when it follows y, j, q, or x.) You will then hear five more words. Put a check next to the number for each word that ends with the -ü sound.

1. _____   2. _____   3. _____   4. _____   5. _____

Audio

II Listening

A. In English, describe the location of each person.

1. _____

2. _____

3. _____

B. Listen to Ellen and Miko's phone call and mark the following statements true (T) or false (F).

	T	F
1. Ellen asks Miko where she is this week.	○	○
2. Miko is at her friend's apartment complex.	○	○
3. Ellen is at home.	○	○
4. Ellen is at school.	○	○

III Speaking

A. Some of Martin and Isabella's future Beijing neighbors travel outside of China during the summer. Look at the calendar below—if today is Friday, who is in China right now and who is in America?

	Owen	Leo	Miko	Ellen	Sanjay	Maya
Friday	美国	美国	中国	中国	中国	美国

IV Reading

A. Read the text conversation between Ellen, Miko, and Leo. Draw a line between each person and their current location.

 Leo, Miko, 你们现在在哪儿？

 我在家。你们也在家吗？

 我也在家。

 我不在家。我现在在学校。

B. Read the dialogue and mark the statements that follow true (T) or false (F).

Emma: 马丁，你现在在家还是在学校？

Martin: 我不在家，也不在学校。

Emma: 你现在在哪儿？

Martin: 我在我同学家。

Emma: 你同学的爸爸和妈妈在不在家？

Martin: 他爸爸在家。他妈妈这个星期在中国。

	T	F
1. Emma asks if Martin is at home or at school.	◯	◯
2. Martin is at his classmate's house.	◯	◯
3. Emma asks if his classmate's older siblings are home.	◯	◯
4. Martin and his classmate are home alone.	◯	◯

C. Read the dialogue and answer the questions below.

Man: 这是谁的宠物？

Woman: 这是我妹妹的宠物。

Man: 那是谁的宠物？

Woman: 那是我哥哥的宠物。

Man: 你喜欢这只宠物还是那只宠物？

Woman: 我不喜欢这只，也不喜欢那只。我不太喜欢宠物。

1. Who has pets?
   (a) the man and the woman
   (b) the woman's older brother
   (c) the woman's younger sister and the woman's older brother

2. Which pet does the woman prefer?
   (a) her younger sister's pet
   (b) her older brother's pet
   (c) neither

3. Who doesn't really like pets?
   (a) the man
   (b) the woman
   (c) the woman's older brother

V Writing

A. Use the words in the list to complete the dialogue. You will use each word only once.

Choices: 对， 美国， 哪儿， 星期， 在， 这个

Student A: 这个 _____ 我不在家。我 _____ 星期 在我朋友的家！

Student B: 他的家在 _____？

Student A: 他的家 _____ 美国！

Student B: 这个星期你在 _____？！

Student A: _____！

B. Rearrange the Chinese words to translate the dialogue.

Person A: Are you in Beijing right now?

_____

北京 ┊ 现在 ┊ 吗？ ┊ 在 ┊ 你

Person B: I'm not in Beijing.

_____

不在 ┊ 我 ┊ 北京。

Person A: Are you in China right now?

_____

吗？ ┊ 你 ┊ 在 ┊ 中国 ┊ 现在

Person B: I'm in China, but I'm not in Beijing.

_____

中国， ┊ 在 ┊ 我 ┊ 不在 ┊ 我 ┊ 可是 ┊ 北京。

Put the Pieces Together!

I Chapter Vocabulary Chart

Fill in the pinyin for and the definition of each word that you learned in this chapter. Use the extra spaces at the end of the chart to add any additional words you learned.

No.	Word	Pinyin	Definition
1	都		
2	学		
3	对		
4	中国		
5	美国		
6	人		
7	这		
8	知道		
9	北京		
10	那		
11	还是		

N	Word	Pinyin	Definition
12	在		
13	哪儿		
14	小区		
15	学校		
16	现在		
17	星期		
18	家		
19			
20			
21			

II Reading

A. Your friend sent you an email! Read the email and then answer the questions below.

我爸爸是中国人。我妈妈是美国人。我的家在美国，可是这个星期我和爸爸都不在美国。你知道我们在哪儿吗？我们在北京！我们现在在我朋友家的小区。我很喜欢北京！我也很喜欢这个小区。

1. Which is true of the writer's parents?
   (a) His mother is Chinese and his father is American.
   (b) His father is Chinese and his mother is American.
   (c) Both his parents are Chinese.

2. Where is the writer's home?
   (a) Beijing
   (b) Shanghai
   (c) America

3. Where is the writer this week?
   (a) Beijing
   (b) Shanghai
   (c) America

4. Where is the writer right now?
   (a) a Chinese school in America
   (b) a neighborhood in Beijing
   (c) his mother's hometown

III Writing

A. Write a short message and try to include at least three of the four elements listed below.

- 都
- A question using 还是
- Where someone is this week
- Where someone is right now

_____

_____

_____

_____

Sports in the Neighborhood

Can-Do Goals

In this chapter, you are learning to:

- Name some sports that are popular in China

- Discuss which sports you can play

- Say where you play sports

- Express whether or not you want to play a sport

- Understand the sports others can and want to play

- Ask if others want to play or watch sports

Playing sports

Audio

I Pinyin and Tone

A. Listen to the tone of each character you hear. Write a 3 next to the characters that are third tone. Write a 1 next to the characters that are first tone.

1. 网 ___   2. 乒 ___   3. 踢 ___   4. 打 ___   5. 有 ___

B. Listen to the recording and number the pinyin in the order the words are spoken. Then draw a line from each pinyin word to the illustration that matches its meaning.

___zúqiú

___pīngpāngqiú

___wǎngqiú

___lánqiú

Audio

II Listening

A. Listen as Owen talks about the sports he and others play. Mark the circles below to show which sports each person can play. Mark all that apply.

	Owen	Owen's younger brother	Maya's younger sister
1. Can play soccer.	○	○	○
2. Can play basketball.	○	○	○
3. Can play tennis.	○	○	○

B. Listen to the man and the woman ta[ ]bout their sports abilities and interests, then mark the following statements true (T) or fa[ ](F).

T F

1. The man likes ping-pong but isn't very [ ]d at it. ○ ○
2. The woman is very good at ping-pong. ○ ○
3. The woman really likes both ping-pong an[ ]nnis. ○ ○
4. The man doesn't know how to play tennis. ○ ○

III Speaking

A. Look at this photo. What can you say about this boy?

IV Reading

A. Read the passage and mark the statements that follow true (T) or false (F).

我会打乒乓球和网球。我哥哥也会打乒乓球和网球。
我姐姐会踢足球，也会打乒乓球。我妹妹会打
乒乓球和篮球。我爸爸和妈妈也会打乒乓球！

	T	F
1. The writer can play ping-pong and basketball.	○	○
2. The writer's older brother can only play ping-pong.	○	○
3. The writer's older sister can play soccer and ping-pong.	○	○
4. The writer's little sister can play tennis and basketball.	○	○
5. The writer's parents can play ping-pong.	○	○
6. Everyone in the family can play ping-pong.	○	○

B. Below is a class schedule for a summer sports school. For the sports you recognize, write the English meanings in the empty column.

Bonus: You will see that the character 球 appears in an unfamiliar sport. Can you guess what 球 means, based on the fact that it is used in the names of so many sports? (Hint: This word in English can also be found in the names of a few well-known sports.)

8:00am–10am	篮球	
10am–12pm	游泳	
1pm–2pm	乒乓球	
2pm–3pm	棒球	
3pm–4pm	击剑	
4pm–5pm	网球	

V | Writing

A. Complete the sentences to indicate which sports these athletes can play.

1. 她会 _____。

2. 他会 _____。

3. 她们会 _____。

4. 他会 _____。

B. Answer the questions according to your own circumstances. Use complete Chinese sentences.

1. 你会打篮球吗?

_____

2. 你会打网球吗?

_____

3. 你会踢足球吗?

_____

Describing a place using 有

Audio

I Pinyin and Tone

A. Listen to the recording and read the pinyin. If the word you hear matches the pinyin, mark the word with a check mark. If the word you hear does not match the pinyin, mark the word with an X. Pay special attention to the tones!

1. zhèr _____   **2.** xiàng _____   **3.** nàr _____   **4.** qù _____   **5.** chàng _____

Audio

II Listening

A. Listen to the man describe the neighborhood where he lives. Circle the facilities his neighborhood has.

1. a school   **3.** a basketball court

2. a soccer field   **4.** a tennis court

B. Listen to each question, then listen to the three possible answers. Mark the letter of the statement that best answers each question.

1. (a) (b) (c)   **3.** (a) (b) (c)

2. (a) (b) (c)   **4.** (a) (b) (c)

C. Two friends have some unexpected free time and are trying to decide how to spend it. Listen to their conversation and answer the questions below.

1. Why does the boy want to go to Wenwen's house?
   (a) He likes Wenwen's older brother.
   (b) He likes Wenwen's pet.

2. At first, where does the girl want to go?
   (a) She wants to go to Chinese school.
   (b) She wants to go to her home.

3. What will the girl probably do at Wenwen's house?
   (a) She will probably study Chinese with Wenwen.
   (b) She will probably play with Wenwen's pet.

III Speaking

A. In Chinese, talk about what sports you think are interesting and uninteresting.

B. Think about the sports facilities at your school. Name one type of field or court that your school has, and one that it doesn't.

IV Reading

A. Read the dialogue and mark the statements that follow true (T) or false (F).

Jingjing: 你想去哪儿？

Chunchun: 我想去学校。那儿有一个篮球场。我想去打篮球。你想去吗？

Jingjing: 我不想去。我觉得打篮球没有意思。我想打网球。可是学校没有网球场。

<table>
<tr><td></td><td>T</td><td>F</td></tr>
<tr><td>1. Chunchun wants to go to their school.</td><td>○</td><td>○</td></tr>
<tr><td>2. Chunchun wants to play tennis at school.</td><td>○</td><td>○</td></tr>
<tr><td>3. Jingjing also wants to go to their school.</td><td>○</td><td>○</td></tr>
<tr><td>4. Jingjing thinks basketball is boring.</td><td>○</td><td>○</td></tr>
<tr><td>5. Chunchun and Jingjing's school has a tennis court.</td><td>○</td><td>○</td></tr>
</table>

B. Read the passage and circle the picture that best matches the writer's description of her neighborhood.

这是我们小区。这儿有一个足球场。我很喜欢去足球场踢足球。这儿有两个网球场，可是没有篮球场。我的学校也在这儿。我很喜欢我的学校！

A. Use the words from the list to complete the sentences. Use each word only once.

Choices: 场，有，那儿，想

1. 我不 _____ 踢足球。

2. _____ 有网球场吗？

3. 这儿没 _____ 篮球场。

4. 我们学校有两个足球 _____。

B. Write a question that is answered by each statement.

1. **A:** 我不想打篮球。

   Q: _____

2. **A:** 没有，这儿没有足球场。

   Q: _____

3. **A:** 我觉得乒乓球很有意思。

   Q: _____

4. **A:** 他们去学校。

   Q: _____

Describing the location of activities

Audio

I Pinyin and Tone

A. The word 在 starts with the z- initial, which sounds much like the "ds" at the end of the English word "beds." Listen to the recording and put a check next to the number of each word that starts with the z- initial.

1. _____ 2. _____ 3. _____ 4. _____ 5. _____

Audio

II Listening

A. Listen to Ellen, Sanjay, and Maya talk about where they frequently play sports. Select the image that best matches what each person says.

1. Ellen (a)   (b)   (c)

2. Sanjay (a)   (b)   (c)

3. Maya (a)   (b)   (c)

B. Listen to each question, then listen to the three possible answers. Mark the letter of the statement that best answers each question.

1. (a) (b) (c)

2. (a) (b) (c)

3. (a) (b) (c)

4. (a) (b) (c)

III Speaking

A. Where does Maya study Chinese, play tennis, and watch basketball games? Using the photographs below as a guide, talk about where Maya does these activities.

IV Reading

A. Read the dialogue, then choose the option that correctly completes each statement.

Miko: 你经常在家看电视吗？

Leo: 对，我很喜欢在家看足球比赛！

Miko: 你会踢足球吗？

Leo: 我不太会踢足球，可是我觉得足球很有意思。我觉得乒乓球也很有意思。我经常在乒乓球馆打乒乓球。

1. Leo frequently watches TV
   (a) at his friend's house.
   (b) at home.

2. Leo
   (a) frequently plays soccer but doesn't often watch soccer games.
   (b) thinks soccer is really interesting, but can't play very well.

3. Leo usually plays ping-pong
   (a) at school.
   (b) at a ping-pong hall.

B. Examine this poster and answer the questions using Chinese.

乒乓球比赛

日期: 06.25
时间: 14:00

XX大学
乒乓球馆

1. What event is this poster advertising?

_____

2. Imagine your friend is participating in this event. What Chinese expression could you use to cheer your friend on?

_____

C. Read the passage, then choose the option that correctly completes each statement. More than one answer may apply.

我们小区有一个中文学校。我很喜欢去那儿学中文。我的同学也很喜欢去那儿学中文。中文学校有中文书和一个电视。我们都很喜欢在那儿看书，也很喜欢在那儿看中文电视。我觉得学中文很有意思！

1. The writer's neighborhood has
   (a) an English school.
   (b) a Chinese school.
   (c) a Chinese sports store.

2. At the school, there are
   (a) Chinese books.
   (b) a TV.
   (c) pets.

3. At the school, the writer likes to
   (a) play ping-pong.
   (b) watch Chinese TV shows.
   (c) read books.

V Writing

A. Rearrange the Chinese words to translate the English sentences.

1. Do you watch basketball games at home?

_____

比赛 ┆ 你 ┆ 看 ┆ 吗？ ┆ 在 ┆ 篮球 ┆ 家

2. I don't play tennis at a basketball court.

_____

打 ┆ 篮球 ┆ 网球。 ┆ 场 ┆ 不在 ┆ 我

3. Do you want to play ping-pong at school?

_____

不想 ┆ 打 ┆ 想 ┆ 学校 ┆ 乒乓球？ ┆ 在 ┆ 你

B. Read the questions and look at the images. Based on the images, create logical answers to the questions.

1. 你想学什么运动？

_____

2. 谁会打乒乓球？

_____

3. 你在篮球馆做什么？

_____

Put the Pieces Together!

I Chapter Vocabulary Chart

Fill in the pinyin for and the definition of the words that you learned in this chapter. Use the extra spaces at the bottom of the chart to add any additional words you learned.

No.	Word	Pinyin	Definition
1	会		
2	打		
3	篮球		
4	乒乓球		
5	踢		
6	足球		
7	网球		
8	这儿		
9	有		
10	场		
11	那儿		

No.	Word	Pinyin	Definition
12	想		
13	去		
14	觉得		
15	有意思		
16	加油		
17	馆		
18	经常		
19	做		
20	运动		
21	在		
22	比赛		

II. Reading

A. Your pen pal from China has written you a letter! Read the letter and mark the statements that follow true (T) or false (F).

我和我的同学都很喜欢看比赛。我们经常在学校的运动场看足球比赛。我也喜欢在家看乒乓球比赛。我很会打乒乓球！我觉得打乒乓球很有意思。你喜欢做什么运动？你和你的同学也喜欢看比赛吗？

	T	F
1. The writer and her classmates really enjoy watching sports matches.	◯	◯
2. The writer is really good at playing tennis.	◯	◯
3. The writer watches sports matches at home and at school.	◯	◯
4. The writer asks what sports you want to learn how to play.	◯	◯

III. Writing

A. Write a response to your pen pal's letter! Be sure to answer the questions that your pen pal posed and remember to ask her at least one question. In addition, try to give your pen pal some additional details about one of the following topics:

- Activities that you frequently do and where you do them
- Sports that you know how to play and where you play them

_____

_____

_____

_____

_____

_____

Appreciating New Sounds

Can-Do Goals

In this chapter, you are learning to:

- Recognize some traditional Chinese musical instruments and their sounds

- Understand when others talk about playing different kinds of instruments

- Say which instruments you play or want to learn to play

- Offer to teach someone something and say who teaches you

- Understand how the words 呢, 啊, and 吧 change the meaning or tone of a sentence

Playing musical instruments

Audio

I Pinyin and Tone

A. Listen to the recording and number the pinyin in the order the words are spoken. Then draw a line from each pinyin word to its English meaning.

____ jítā	**a.** to pull, to play an instrument
____ èrhú	**b.** to blow, to play an instrument
____ lā	**c.** guitar
____ chuī	**d.** erhu
____ gǔzhēng	**e.** to strum, to pluck, to play an instrument
____ dízi	**f.** guzheng
____ tán	**g.** flute

Audio

II Listening

A. Listen as Ellen, Miko, and Leo say which instruments they can and cannot play. Mark the circle if the person can play the instrument.

		Erhu	Guitar
1.	Ellen	○	○
2.	Miko	○	○
3.	Leo	○	○

B. You will hear four people talk about the instrument(s) they can play. Write the letter of the image that matches each description you hear.

1. ____   2. ____   3. ____   4. ____

a

b

c

d

III Speaking

A. Imagine that a new store selling Chinese musical instruments has opened in your area, and the owner is offering lessons. Using Chinese, how would you tell the owner you want to learn guzheng?

B. Look at this photo of students hanging out. What can you say about the student with the guitar? What else can you say in Chinese about the image?

IV Reading

A. Read the passage, then draw a line between each person and the instrument he or she wants to learn.

我，我姐姐和我妹妹都想学乐器。我想学拉二胡。我姐姐想学弹古筝。我和我姐姐都很喜欢中国乐器。可是我妹妹不喜欢中国乐器。她不想学拉二胡，也不想学弹古筝。她想学弹吉他。

1. The writer   **2.** The writer's older sister   **3.** The writer's younger sister

a

b

c

B. Read the passage and mark the statements that follow true (T) or false (F).

Man: 你会不会拉二胡？

Woman: 会，我会拉二胡。我也会弹古筝。
你会什么乐器？

Man: 我不会中国乐器，可是我会弹吉他。

Woman: 弹吉他有意思吗？

Man: 很有意思！你想学弹吉他吗？

Woman: 我不太想学弹吉他。我想学吹笛子。
谁会吹笛子？你知道吗？

Man: 我不知道。

	T	F
1. Neither the man nor the woman can play the erhu.	○	○
2. Both the man and the woman can play the guzheng.	○	○
3. The woman wants to learn to play the guitar.	○	○
4. Neither the man nor the woman can play the flute.	○	○

V **Writing**

A. What instrument can you play or do you want to learn to play? Write a complete Chinese sentence that answers the question according to your own circumstances.

_____

B. Rearrange the Chinese words to translate the English sentences.

1. Do you want to learn to play the erhu?

_____

学 ┊ 想 ┊ 你 ┊ 拉 ┊ 不想 ┊ 二胡?

2. I think playing guitar is really fun.

_____

有意思。 ┊ 觉得 ┊ 弹 ┊ 我 ┊ 吉他 ┊ 很

3. My friend is very good at playing the flute.

_____

吹 ┊ 会 ┊ 很 ┊ 笛子。 ┊ 我 ┊ 朋友

4. Can your Chinese teacher play the guzheng?

_____

中文 ┊ 不会 ┊ 老师 ┊ 会 ┊ 古筝? ┊ 弹 ┊ 你的

5. What instruments can you play?

_____

乐器? ┊ 会 ┊ 你们 ┊ 什么

Exclamations, suggestions, and questions

Audio

I Pinyin and Tone

A. Look at the following pairs of words that sound identical except for the tone. You will hear one word from each pair; circle the word you hear.

1. (a) 是 shì   (b) 十 shí
2. (a) 区 qū   (b) 去 qù
3. (a) 哪儿 nǎr   (b) 那儿 nàr
4. (a) 买 mǎi   (b) 卖 mài

B. The characters 啊 , 吧 , and 呢 are all examples of neutral tone characters. Neutral tone characters usually come right after another character. Listen to the following words and phrases and circle all that have a neutral tone at the end.

1. 什么   2. 可是   3. 觉得   4. 名字   5. 古筝   6. 加油

Audio

II Listening

A. Listen to the dialogue and mark the following statements true (T) or false (F).

	T	F
1. The conversation probably takes place at a musical instrument store.	○	○
2. The woman knows exactly what instrument she wants.	○	○
3. The man suggests that the woman buy an erhu.	○	○
4. The man is a guzheng teacher.	○	○

B. Listen to each question, then listen to the three possible answers. Mark the letter of the statement that best answers each question.

1. (a) (b) (c)

2. (a) (b) (c)

3. (a) (b) (c)

C. Listen to the conversation at a pet store and answer the questions below.

1. What does the man want to buy?
   - (a) one pet
   - (b) two pets
   - (c) three pets

2. What kind of pet does the man want to buy?
   - (a) a dog
   - (b) a cat
   - (c) unknown

3. What pet does the man buy in the end?
   - (a) this pet
   - (b) that pet
   - (c) neither pet

III Speaking

A. Your friend wants to buy an instrument and needs help deciding which one to choose. Make a suggestion in Chinese as to which of the instruments pictured below he should buy.

IV Reading

A. Read the dialogue and mark the statements that follow true (T) or false (F).

Ellen: 你想买乐器吗？

Maya: 想啊。我想买古筝。你呢？

Ellen: 我不想买古筝。我想买二胡。

Maya: 我们现在去乐器店吧！

Ellen: 好啊。你知道不知道乐器店在哪儿？

Maya: 你看！那儿有一个乐器店。我们去那儿吧！

Ellen: 可是那个乐器店不卖中国乐器。

	T	F
1. Both girls want to buy a musical instrument.	○	○
2. Ellen wants to buy a guzheng.	○	○
3. Maya suggests they go buy instruments right now.	○	○
4. Maya sees a musical instrument store nearby.	○	○
5. The musical instrument store only sells Chinese musical instruments.	○	○

B. Andy is out shopping. Read his conversations with two different shop owners, then mark the statements that follow true (T) or false (F).

Andy enters the first shop.

Andy:	你好，这儿卖古筝吗？
Shop Owner 1:	我们不卖古筝啊。我们卖吉他。
Andy:	可是我想买古筝……
Shop Owner 1:	你去那个店吧。那个店卖古筝。
Andy:	好啊！

Andy enters a second shop.

Andy:	你好！这儿卖古筝，对吗？
Shop Owner 2:	对啊！
Andy:	我想买古筝。
Shop Owner 2:	好啊！
Andy:	你会弹古筝吗？
Shop Owner 2:	我会。你呢？
Andy:	我不会。我很想学古筝。

		T	F
1.	The first store sells guitars but not guzhengs.	○	○
2.	Andy wants to buy a guitar and a guzheng.	○	○
3.	Both Andy and the owner of the second shop can play the guzheng.	○	○

A. Complete the sentences below by adding 啊 , 吧 , or 呢 .

1. 我想学古筝。你 ___ ?

2. 我们去那个店 ___ !

3. 我的朋友都会乐器。你的朋友 ___ ?

4. 你很会拉二胡 ___ !

5. 那儿有一个足球场。我们去踢足球 ___ !

6. 你有六个妹妹 ___ !

B. Each photo below shows someone suggesting something. Caption each photo in Chinese with the suggestion being made, using 吧 .

_____   _____

Teaching and learning musical instruments

I Pinyin and Tone

Audio

A. When two third tone characters appear next to each other, either in a word or phrase, the first one is pronounced as a second tone. Read the following words and listen to the recording. In the recording, you will hear two pronunciations for each word. Mark the letter of the pronunciation that is correct for the characters you see.

1. 可以   (a)   (b)

2. 你好   (a)   (b)

3. 很好   (a)   (b)

4. 也有   (a)   (b)

II Listening

Audio

A. Listen to the dialogue and mark the following statements true (T) or false (F).

	T	F
1. The woman likes listening to music.	○	○
2. The woman can only play one instrument.	○	○
3. The man can play a musical instrument.	○	○
4. The man wants to learn the guzheng.	○	○
5. The woman agrees to teach him.	○	○

B. Listen to the dialogue and mark the following statements true (T) or false (F).

	T	F
1. Mr. Li teaches guzheng.	○	○
2. The man wants to learn the erhu.	○	○
3. The woman teaches the instrument that the man wants to learn.	○	○
4. The man doesn't want to learn from the woman.	○	○

III Speaking

A. Think of something you can do. Use Chinese to say who taught you to do that thing. Then use Chinese to offer to teach someone else how to do that thing.

B. Imagine you want to listen to music during Chinese class. Using Chinese, how would you ask your teacher for permission?

IV Reading

A. Examine this screenshot of a music school website to find out which instruments each teacher can teach. Mark the circles accordingly.

星星 音乐学校

马老师
吉他, 小提琴,
尤克里里

李老师
二胡, 古筝, 笛子

林老师
吉他, 笛子, 鼓

	Mr. Ma	Ms. Li	Ms. Lin
1. Teaches the guitar.	○	○	○
2. Teaches the flute.	○	○	○
3. Teaches the erhu.	○	○	○
4. Teaches the guzheng.	○	○	○

B. Read the dialogue and mark the statements that follow true (T) or false (F).

Younger sister: 姐姐，你是音乐老师，对吧？

Older sister: 对啊！

Younger sister: 你可以教我弹吉他吗？

Older sister: 不可以……我不想教你。

Younger sister: 你教我吧，姐姐！我很想学吉他！

Older sister: 可是我不太会弹吉他……你去音乐学校学吧。李老师可以教你。他很会弹吉他。

	T	F
1. The older sister is a music teacher.	○	○
2. The younger sister wants to learn the erhu.	○	○
3. The older sister is willing to teach the younger sister.	○	○
4. Mr. Li can play the guitar.	○	○

C. Read the passage and mark the statements that follow true (T) or false (F).

我爸爸是中国人。他很喜欢音乐。他经常在家听音乐。他是中国音乐学校的老师。他在那儿教学生吹笛子。这个星期我爸爸不在中国。他在美国教笛子。他的美国学生也很喜欢学中国乐器。他们都觉得中国乐器很有意思。

	T	F
1. The writer's father is Chinese and really likes music.	○	○
2. The writer's father frequently listens to music at home.	○	○
3. The writer's father is a teacher at a Chinese music school.	○	○
4. The writer's father is in America teaching guzheng this week.	○	○
5. According to the writer, his father's American students aren't very interested in learning to play Chinese instruments.	○	○

V Writing

A. Rearrange the Chinese words to translate the English sentences.

1. Do you like listening to music?

_____

喜欢 ┆ 听 ┆ 吗? ┆ 你 ┆ 音乐

2. Who teaches you to play the guzheng?

_____

古筝? ┆ 教 ┆ 你 ┆ 谁 ┆ 弹

3. Can Mr. Li teach my younger brother to play the erhu?

_____

二胡 ┆ 可以 ┆ 弟弟 ┆ 李老师 ┆ 我 ┆ 教 ┆ 吗? ┆ 拉

B. Imagine that in addition to teaching Chinese, your Chinese instructor is also a skilled erhu player. Compose an email message in Chinese asking your Chinese teacher to teach you the erhu. Try to begin the email with a greeting and end it with "thank you."

_____

_____

_____

_____

Put the Pieces Together!

I Chapter Vocabulary Chart

Fill in the pinyin for and the definition of each word that you learned in this chapter. Use the extra spaces at the end of the chart to add any additional words you learned.

No.	Word	Pinyin	Definition
1	弹		
2	吉他		
3	乐器		
4	古筝		
5	拉		
6	二胡		
7	吹		
8	笛子		
9	呢		
10	店		
11	卖		

No.	Word	Pinyin	Definition
12	买		
13	吧		
14	啊		
15	听		
16	音乐		
17	可以		
18	教		
19	谢谢		

II Reading

A. Read the passage and then answer the questions that follow.

我很会弹古筝。我在一个音乐学校教古筝。我妈妈也在那个音乐学校教乐器。她教笛子。你想学弹古筝吗？我可以教你！你想学吹笛子吗？我妈妈可以教你！我爸爸在一个乐器店卖中国乐器。你想买中国乐器吗？你去那个乐器店吧！你可以在那儿买二胡，笛子和古筝。

1. Where does the writer teach the guzheng?
    (a) at a middle school
    (b) at a musical instrument store
    (c) at a music school

2. What does the writer's mother do?
    (a) sells Chinese musical instruments at a musical instrument store
    (b) teaches the guzheng at a music school
    (c) teaches the flute at a music school

3. What does the writer's father do?
    (a) sells guitars at a musical instrument store
    (b) sells Chinese instruments at a musical instrument store
    (c) teaches the erhu at a music school

4. Which is NOT sold at the musical instrument store?
    (a) a guitar
    (b) an erhu
    (c) a guzheng

III Writing

Write a short paragraph about what instruments you or someone you know likes, can play, and wants to learn. Use the writing checklist below as a guide. (Ask your teacher or refer to the chart below for the names of additional instruments.)

- 我喜欢……
- 我会弹 / 吹 / 拉……
- 我想学……

_____

_____

_____

_____

吹 (chuī) To blow, to play	黑管 (hēiguǎn)	clarinet
	萨克斯 (sàkèsī)	saxophone
弹 (tán) To strum, to pluck, to play	钢琴 (gāngqín)	piano
	尤克里里 (yóukèlǐlǐ)	ukulele
拉 (lā) To pull, to play	小提琴 (xiǎotíqín)	violin
	大提琴 (dàtíqín)	cello
打 To hit, to play	鼓 (gǔ)	drums

Do You Have Plans?

Can-Do Goals

In this chapter, you are learning to:

- State the date and the day of the week of an upcoming activity

- Understand numbers larger than ten

- Discuss when you are free

- Ask and answer questions about birthdays

- Talk about buying a gift based on someone's interests

Scheduling an activity

Audio

I Pinyin and Tone

A. Listen to the recording and write the pinyin for each word you hear. Then draw a line from each pinyin word to its meaning in English.

1. _____　　　**a.** Thursday

2. _____　　　**b.** Wednesday

3. _____　　　**c.** Sunday

4. _____　　　**d.** Tuesday

5. _____　　　**e.** Monday

6. _____　　　**f.** Friday

7. _____　　　**g.** Saturday

Audio

II Listening

A. Listen to the girl talk about her schedule, then circle the correct activity for each day.

1. Thursday	2. Friday	3. Saturday	4. Sunday
free time	play guzheng	play tennis	see a movie
OR	OR	OR	OR
study Chinese	play guitar	play basketball	free time

B. Listen to each question, then listen to the three possible answers. Mark the letter of the statement that best answers each question.

1. (a) (b) (c)

2. (a) (b) (c)

3. (a) (b) (c)

C. Listen to the dialogue and mark the following statements true (T) or false (F).

	T	F
1. The boy asks the girl if she wants to play basketball today.	○	○
2. The girl wants to watch an American movie.	○	○
3. The boy doesn't want to watch an American movie because he doesn't like them.	○	○
4. The boy suggests they go watch a ping pong competition.	○	○

III Speaking

A. Imagine that you are going to ask your Chinese friend 春春 to see a movie with you this weekend. Take a look at these pages from her schedule, then, in Chinese, extend an invitation on a day when she has free time.

B. 春春 just realized she already has plans for that day! She suggests you see the movie on Monday. How would you respond? Do you have free time?

IV Reading

A. You are planning a visit to a museum in China. Answer the questions below based on the museum's online ticket-booking calendar and the information given about Isabella, Martin, and Daming's schedules. You may use English to answer the questions.

春月星期一、星期三、星期五和星期天有空。

马丁星期一、星期二、星期三和星期四有空。

大明星期四和星期六有空。

Note: The bottom row of numbers shows how many tickets are available for each day.

1. If you wanted to go to the museum with both Martin and Isabella, which day would you reserve tickets for?

_____

2. If you wanted to visit the museum with Daming, on which day would you go?

_____

B. Read the dialogue and mark the statements that follow true (T) or false (F).

Miko: 马丁，你星期二有空吗？我想星期二去拉二胡。你去不去？

Martin: 星期二我没有空。我想星期三去拉二胡。你星期三有空吗？

Miko: 星期三我没有空……

Martin: 星期四你有空吗？

Miko: 有空！我们星期四去拉二胡吧！

Martin: 好啊！

	T	F
1. Miko wants to go play the erhu with Martin on Monday.	○	○
2. Martin doesn't have free time on the day Miko first suggests.	○	○
3. Miko can't play the erhu on Wednesday because she has no free time.	○	○
4. Miko and Martin agree to play the erhu on Friday.	○	○

V Writing

A. Use the words and phrases in the list to complete the sentences. Use each word/phrase only once.

Choices: 星期五，后天，几，有空，没有空

Li Ming: 今天是星期三。后天是星期 _____ ？

Bai Ying: _____ 是星期五。

Li Ming: 你星期五 _____ 吗？

Bai Ying: 有！我 _____ 、星期六都有空。你呢？

Li Ming: 星期五我有空，可是星期六我 _____ 。

B. Your Chinese friend 丁国 has emailed asking if you have any free time this Saturday, but you don't! You have free time this Sunday. How would you tell him your schedule in Chinese? Write your answer on the line below.

Talking about birthdays

Audio

I Pinyin and Tone

A. Listen to the recording and number the pinyin in the order the words are spoken. Then draw a line from each pinyin word to its meaning.

____ èrshísān	**a.** 17
____ wǔshí	**b.** 90
____ shíqī	**c.** 31
____ sānshíyī	**d.** 26
____ jiǔshí	**e.** 50
____ èrshíliù	**f.** 23

Audio

II Listening

A. You will hear the birthdays of Chinese-born actress Gong Li, Chinese basketball player Yao Ming, and Chinese-American author Amy Tan. Using English, write their birthdays in the following format: month date. (Example: October 8)

Gong Li

Birthday: _____

Yao Ming

Birthday: _____

Amy Tan

Birthday: _____

B. Listen to each question, then listen to the three possible answers. Mark the letter of the statement that best answers each question.

1. (a) (b) (c)

2. (a) (b) (c)

3. (a) (b) (c)

III Speaking

A. Your Chinese friend has just asked you when your birthday is. Using Chinese, how will you respond?

B. Take a look at Isabella's list of birthdays. In complete Chinese sentences, give the names and birthdays of those whose birthdays are NOT during the summer months.

Birthdays

Martin - 3/15
Miko - 6/21
Ellen - 7/9
Maya - 7/13
Mom - 7/18
Owen - 8/1
Leo - 11/29
Sanjay - 12/14

IV Reading

A. Read the passage and fill in the calendar with the birthdays of the writer and the writer's siblings. Mark the older brother's birthday with an X, the older sister's birthday with a check, the younger sister's birthday with a circle, and the writer's birthday with a star.

我有一个哥哥，一个姐姐和一个妹妹。我的生日是六月三号。我哥哥的生日是六月十七号。我姐姐的生日是七月二十一号。我妹妹的生日是七月三十号。

2025						六月
日	一	二	三	四	五	六
1	2	3	4	5	6	7
8	9	10	11	12	13	14
15	16	17	18	19	20	21
22	23	24	25	26	27	28
29	30					

2025						七月
日	一	二	三	四	五	六
		1	2	3	4	5
6	7	8	9	10	11	12
13	14	15	16	17	18	19
20	21	22	23	24	25	26
27	28	29	30	31		

B. Read the dialogue, then choose the option that correctly completes each sentence.

Mingming: 你的生日是几月几号？

Huanhuan: 十月二十八号。你的呢？

Mingming: 我的生日是下个星期五！

Huanhuan: 下个星期五是你的生日啊！你想做什么？

Mingming: 我想去看电影。你有空吗？你想不想去看电影？

Huanhuan: 有空！我也想去看电影！

1. Huanhuan's birthday is
   (a) October 12th.
   (b) October 28th.
   (c) November 28th.

2. Mingming's birthday is
   (a) we don't know when.
   (b) next Friday.
   (c) this Saturday.

3. For his birthday, Mingming wants to
   (a) go play ping-pong.
   (b) go play basketball.
   (c) go see a movie.

4. Huanhuan
   (a) has free time and also wants to go see a movie.
   (b) has free time but doesn't want to go see a movie.
   (c) doesn't have free time.

C. Read the dialogue and answer the questions that follow.

 你周末经常做什么？

 我经常打网球，弹吉他，看电影。你呢？

 我不会打网球，也不会弹吉他。我周末经常在家看电视。可是我觉得看电视很没有意思。

 打网球和弹吉他都很有意思。你想学吗？这个周末我可以教你。

 我想打网球！可是这个周末我没有空。下个周末你可以教我吗？

 可以啊！

1. Which of the following does Maya frequently do on weekends?
   (a) play basketball
   (b) play guitar
   (c) watch TV

2. What does Owen say he thinks is boring?
   (a) playing tennis
   (b) playing guitar
   (c) watching TV at home

3. What does Maya offer to do for Owen?
   (a) watch a movie with him
   (b) teach him tennis and guitar
   (c) buy him a guitar

4. What does Owen tell Maya that he is interested in learning?
   (a) tennis
   (b) guitar
   (c) neither

A. On the line below, write a complete sentence giving the birthday of a friend or family member.

_____

B. You're checking the weather forecast for next week to decide on plans. Keeping the weather and your own preferences in mind, answer the questions below in complete Chinese sentences. Choose a different day next week for each activity.

6 号 星期日	7 号 星期一	8 号 星期二	9 号 星期三	10 号 星期四	11 号 星期五	12 号 星期六
64°	72°	83°	78°	74°	74°	68°

1. On what day next week do you want to go watch a movie?

_____

2. On what day next week do you want to go play soccer?

_____

Reacting to new information

I Pinyin and Tone

Audio

A. Listen as each word is read and write the correct pinyin (including tone marks). Then draw a line from each pinyin word to its meaning in English.

1. _____

2. _____

3. _____

4. _____

5. _____

a. in that case, then

b. to ask (a question)

c. month, moon

d. to be free, to have free time

e. day of the month

B. The word 礼物 (lǐwù) has a third tone-fourth tone pattern. Listen to the recording. You will hear the word 礼物 (lǐwù) followed by five more words. Put a check next to each word that shares the third tone-fourth tone pattern.

1. 比赛 __   2. 生日 __   3. 北京 __   4. 早上 __   5. 好看 __

II Listening

Audio

A. Listen to the dialogue and mark the following statements true (T) or false (F).

	T	F
1. The man says that his birthday is coming up.	○	○
2. The birthday is the day after tomorrow.	○	○
3. The woman and the man will go shopping for a birthday present right now.	○	○

B. Listen to the conversation between Ellen and Martin, then mark the following statements true (T) or false (F).

	T	F
1. Ellen asks Martin if Isabella likes to play basketball.	○	○
2. Ellen's gift for Isabella is a basketball.	○	○
3. Martin thinks Isabella might not like Ellen's gift.	○	○

A. You've asked your Chinese friends if they want to go see a movie on Friday, but they all have to study English. In reaction to this new information, refer to the schedule of showtimes below and suggest a different day to see the movie instead. Remember: Use 那 to react to the new information!

Riding Around Beijing
🕐 2hrs 10min

Mingming is looking forward to a relaxing bicycle tour of Beijing...instead, he's in for a day full of adventures and mishaps!

| Friday | Saturday | Sunday |

IV Reading

A. Below are three sentences, each followed by three possible responses. Choose the best response to each sentence.

1. 马丁喜欢看书吗?

   (a) 我不知道,你问他姐姐吧。

   (b) 马丁是我的同学。

   (c) 马丁不想去买书。

2. 我这个周末没有空。

   (a) 那我们学中文吧。

   (b) 那你下个周末有空吗?

   (c) 那我们这个周末去买礼物吧。

3. 下个周末你们去看电影吗?

   (a) 这个周末我们不去看电影。

   (b) 下个周末我们一定去看书。

   (c) 下个周末我们一定去看电影。

B. Read the dialogue and answer the questions that follow.

 下个周末那个乒乓球馆有乒乓球比赛。你想去看吗？

 下个周末我没有空……

 那你弟弟呢？他有空吗？

 他也没有空。下个周末我和我弟弟都没有空。你去问春月吧。她觉得乒乓球很有意思。她一定想去看乒乓球比赛。

 好主意！那我问她吧。

1. What does Leo want to do, and when does he want to do it?
   (a) Leo wants to play ping-pong next weekend.
   (b) Leo wants to play ping-pong this weekend.
   (c) Leo wants to watch a ping-pong match next weekend.

2. Besides Owen, who else won't have time next weekend?
   (a) Isabella also won't have time next weekend.
   (b) Owen's friend also won't have time next weekend.
   (c) Owen's younger brother also won't have time next weekend.

3. Why will Isabella definitely be interested in Leo's invitation?
   (a) Isabella thinks ping-pong is very interesting, so she'll definitely want to watch the match.
   (b) Isabella thinks ping-pong is very interesting, so she'll definitely want to play.
   (c) Isabella always has free time, so she'll definitely want to watch the match.

V Writing

A. Rearrange the Chinese words to create logical sentences.

1. _____

有空 ┊ 周末 ┊ 吗? ┊ 李老师

2. _____

我 ┊ 知道。 ┊ 不 ┊ 也

3. _____

觉得 ┊ 我 ┊ 一定 ┊ 他 ┊ 不 ┊ 有空。

4. _____

他 ┊ 吧! ┊ 我们 ┊ 学校 ┊ 去 ┊ 那 ┊ 问

5. _____

主意! ┊ 好

B. Create a logical dialogue by writing the missing sentence. Try to use 那 in your sentence.

Maya: 你喜欢看电影吗?

Ellen: 喜欢!

Maya: _____

Ellen: 好啊!

Put the Pieces Together!

I Chapter Vocabulary Chart

Fill in the pinyin for and the definition of each word that you learned in this chapter. Use the extra spaces at the end of the chart to add any additional words you learned.

No.	Word	Pinyin	Definition
1	今天		
2	星期五		
3	电影		
4	有空		
5	明天		
6	后天		
7	生日		
8	月		
9	号		
10	六月		
11	二十一		

No.	Word	Pinyin	Definition
12	下个		
13	周末		
14	礼物		
15	那		
16	问		
17	一定		
18	主意		

II Reading

A. Read the dialogue and answer the questions that follow.

Tongtong: 下个星期六是七月五号，也是文文的生日。可是我不知道她喜欢什么礼物。

Jingjing: 我问你，她喜欢看电影吗？

Tongtong: 我不知道。

Jingjing: 她喜欢听音乐吗？

Tongtong: 我也不知道。

Jingjing: 那她喜欢做运动吗？

Tongtong: 喜欢。她经常在学校踢足球。

Jingjing: 那你这个周末有空吗？你去买一个足球吧！

Tongtong: 好主意！她一定喜欢这个生日礼物。谢谢！

1. When is Wenwen's birthday?
   (a) next Saturday, July 5th
   (b) next Friday, June 7th
   (c) next Sunday, May 6th

2. Does Wenwen like watching movies?
   (a) Yes, she likes watching American movies.
   (b) No, she doesn't like watching movies.
   (c) We don't know if she likes watching movies.

3. Does Wenwen like listening to music?
   (a) Yes, she likes listening to Chinese music.
   (b) No, she doesn't like listening to music.
   (c) We don't know if she likes listening to music.

4. Does Wenwen like sports?
   (a) Yes, she likes sports.
   (b) No, she doesn't like sports.
   (c) We don't know if she likes sports.

5. What will Tongtong buy as a birthday present for Wenwen?
   (a) Tongtong will buy a movie ticket.
   (b) Tongtong will buy a soccer ball.
   (c) Tongtong will buy a musical instrument.

A. Your friend 春春 is texting you. Reply to her messages to create a complete conversation.

春春： 你知道后天是几月几号吗？

我： _____

春春： 那你知道不知道后天是我的生日？

我： _____

我： _____

春春： 想，可是我后天没有空。

我： _____

春春： 好啊！

我： _____

春春： 你想送我一个礼物？谢谢！你可以问我姐姐。
她一定知道！

If you need help thinking of responses, consider including some of the following words and phrases:

- 想不想
- 那
- 吧
- 喜欢什么礼物

Shopping for the Perfect Gift

Can-Do Goals   In this chapter, you are learning to:

- Understand when others describe what they are going to do

- Talk about when you are busy and when you plan to do certain activities

- Use appropriate greetings for phone conversations

- Agree or disagree with someone

- Discuss purchasing a gift for someone

- Give simple descriptions of books and clothes

Times of day

Audio

I Pinyin and Tone

A. Listen to the recording and add the correct tone mark to the pinyin for each syllable.

1. wu   **2.** wan   **3.** xia   **4.** zao   **5.** shang   **6.** wei

Audio

II Listening

A. Listen to Sanjay and Isabella's conversation and mark the following statements true (T) or false (F).

	T	F
1. The conversation likely takes place over the phone.	○	○
2. Isabella has things to do in the morning but not in the afternoon.	○	○
3. Isabella has free time in the evening.	○	○

B. Listen to the dialogue and answer the questions that follow.

1. Which of the following questions does the woman ask the man?
(a) Do you have free time today?
(b) Do you like movies?
(c) Do you want to go see a movie?

2. Which of the following statements is true?
(a) The man has no free time at all tomorrow.
(b) The man has things to do tomorrow evening but is free the rest of the day.
(c) The man is free at noon tomorrow.

III Speaking

A. Take a look at the page from Martin's planner. In Chinese, talk about what times of day he is free and what times of day he has things to do.

B. Imagine that you want to call Martin and invite him to see a movie with you. How would you ask him in Chinese? Greet him first, then make sure to mention the specific time of day you want to go see a movie!

Thursday	07/17
9:00	Chinese class
10:00	Practice writing in Chinese
11:00	↓
12:00	Get lunch with friends
1:00	
2:00	
3:00	
4:00	
5:00	Swim practice
6:00	↓
7:00	Meet friends at park
8:00	Read
Note:	ask Daming for music recs

IV Reading

A. Read Jingjing's schedule for the coming weekend, then mark the statements that follow true (T) or false (F).

	星期五	星期六	星期天
早上	有事	有空	有空
上午	打网球	打篮球	打乒乓球
中午	学中文	有空	有空
下午	买礼物	有空	看乒乓球比赛
晚上	有空	看电影	有事

	T	F
1. Jingjing has free time on Friday evening, Saturday afternoon, and Sunday noon.	○	○
2. Jingjing will watch a movie on Saturday evening.	○	○
3. Jingjing will play sports every afternoon.	○	○
4. Jingjing will watch a ping-pong match on Sunday morning.	○	○

B. Read the dialogue and answer the questions that follow.

Maya: 喂，早上好，春月。我是 Maya。你现在有空吗？

Isabella: 早上好，Maya。我现在有空。有什么事吗？

Maya: 明天是 Owen 的生日。我今天要去买生日礼物。你去不去？

Isabella: 去！我今天下午有空。我们可以下午去吗？

Maya: 今天下午我有事。今天晚上你有空吗？

Isabella: 有。那我们今天晚上去买礼物吧！

Maya: 好啊！晚上见。

1. Why did Maya call Isabella?
   (a) because she wants Isabella to go to the movies with her
   (b) because she wants Isabella to go with her to buy a birthday present for Owen
   (c) because it's Isabella's birthday

2. When does Isabella initially suggest they go?
   (a) this afternoon
   (b) this evening
   (c) tomorrow morning

3. When do Isabella and Maya agree to go?
   (a) this afternoon
   (b) this evening
   (c) tomorrow morning

4. Based on the context, what do you think Isabella's question "有什么事吗" means?
   (a) When do you have free time?
   (b) What item do you have?
   (c) What's up?

A. Rearrange the Chinese words given to complete the sentences. The first and last words of each sentence have been placed for you.

1. 你 _____ 电影？

看 ｜ 要 ｜ 什么

2. 今天 _____ 事。

有 ｜ 下午 ｜ 我

3. 明天 _____ 中文。

要 ｜ 我 ｜ 早上 ｜ 学

4. 你们 _____ 电影？

晚上 ｜ 看 ｜ 不要 ｜ 后天 ｜ 要

5. 那 _____ 吧！

下午 ｜ 我们 ｜ 见 ｜ 星期六

B. Your Chinese friend has just sent you a message. How will you respond?

京京

早上好啊！今天
上午你有空吗？

我：_____

Shopping choices

I Pinyin and Tone

Audio

A. The character 本 ends with the -en final and 难 ends with the -an final. Listen to each character you hear. Underline the characters that end with -en. Circle the characters that end with -an.

1. 问   2. 晚   3. 人   4. 单   5. 看   6. 很

II Listening

Audio

A. You will hear four books being described. Write the letter of the image that matches each description you hear.

1. ___   2. ___   3. ___   4. ___

B. Listen to the dialogue and mark the following statements true (T) or false (F).

	T	F
1. The man asks the woman if she wants to buy a book.	○	○
2. The man says the book is inexpensive but difficult.	○	○
3. The woman thinks the book is interesting.	○	○
4. The woman doesn't want to buy the book.	○	○

C. Listen to the dialogue and answer the questions below.

1. Which of the following statements is true?
   (a) Both the man and the woman like listening to guzheng, but neither can play it.
   (b) The woman likes guzheng and can play it, but the man doesn't like guzheng.
   (c) Both the man and the woman like guzheng, but only the woman can play it.

2. According to the conversation, is guzheng difficult to learn?
   (a) Yes, it is very difficult to learn.
   (b) No. According to the woman, it isn't difficult.
   (c) Neither the man nor the woman mention if guzheng is difficult to learn.

3. Based on the end of the conversation, what do you think the man is most likely to do?
   (a) He is likely to buy a guzheng and learn how to play it from the woman.
   (b) He is likely to try listening to guzheng music even though he doesn't like it much.
   (c) He is likely to learn guzheng from the woman, but he won't buy his own.

III Speaking

A. Your Chinese friend has just asked if you want to buy the book below. How would you respond? Give a reason why you would or would not want to buy the book below.

B. Your friend wants your advice as to which of the instruments below she should buy. Keeping in mind the prices and the instruments you think are interesting, which instrument would you tell your friend to buy? Make a suggestion in Chinese and also give a reason for that suggestion.

$20

$100

$40

A. Read the dialogue and answer the questions that follow.

Martin: 你好！这儿有没有简单而且有意思的中文书？

Bookseller: 有。你看，这本书和那本书都很有意思。

Martin: 这本书很难而且很贵。我不想买这本书。

Bookseller: 那本书很简单，也很便宜。

Martin: 那我买那本书吧。

1. What is Martin hoping to buy?
   (a) an interesting English book
   (b) a simple and interesting Chinese book
   (c) an inexpensive and interesting Chinese book

2. What does the bookseller show Martin?
   (a) two interesting and inexpensive books
   (b) two inexpensive but difficult books
   (c) two interesting books

3. What does Martin think of the books the bookseller shows him?
   (a) Martin likes both books.
   (b) Martin thinks one of the books is boring.
   (c) Martin thinks one of the books is difficult and also expensive.

4. In the end, what does Martin decide to buy?
   (a) an interesting book that is simple and also inexpensive
   (b) two interesting books
   (c) a book that is difficult but inexpensive

B. Read the paragraph and answer the questions that follow.

我今天上午，下午和晚上都有事。上午我要去学校学中文。我觉得中文很有意思，而且不太难。下午我要去学校书店买一本中文书。我有中文书，可是它们都很难，而且没有意思。学校书店的书很便宜，而且很简单。晚上我要做什么？你知道吗？我要看书！

1. Which of the following statements is true?
   (a) The writer has things to do this morning, at noon, and this evening.
   (b) The writer has things to do at noon, this afternoon, and this evening.
   (c) The writer has things to do this morning, this afternoon, and this evening.

2. Which of the following statements is NOT true?
   (a) The writer will study Chinese at school in the morning and read books at home in the evening.
   (b) The writer will go to the school bookstore in the afternoon and read at home in the evening.
   (c) The writer will study Chinese at school in the morning, but he doesn't like it very much.

3. Which of the following statements is true?
   (a) The writer thinks Chinese is simple but boring.
   (b) The writer thinks Chinese is interesting and not too difficult.
   (c) The writer thinks Chinese is interesting but very difficult.

4. Which of these is a reason the writer wants to buy books at the school bookstore?
   (a) The books he has at home are too easy and are also boring.
   (b) The books at the school book store are inexpensive and also difficult.
   (c) The books he has at home are difficult and also boring.

V Writing

A. Complete each sentence so that it accurately describes the image. Use the words in the list to help you. You will use some words more than once.

Choices: 便宜，贵，简单，难，很

1. 这本书 _____ 。

2. 这本书 _____ 。

3. 这本书 _____ ，
而且 _____ 。

B. Think of a book you've read recently and write a short review of it. In your review, mention whether you like the book and try to use two description words.

_____

Buying clothes

I Pinyin and Tone

Audio

A. The word 颜色 (yánsè) has a second tone-fourth tone pattern. Listen to the following five words and put a check next to each word that also has a second tone-fourth tone pattern.

1. 同意___ 2. 简单___ 3. 一定___ 4. 十月___ 5. 中午___

II Listening

Audio

A. Listen to the conversation and answer the questions below.

1. What does the girl give the boy?
   (a) an interesting book
   (b) a nice-looking piece of clothing
   (c) a basketball

2. Does the boy seem to like his gift?
   (a) yes, because he likes the color
   (b) yes, because he likes playing basketball
   (c) no, because he doesn't like reading

B. Listen to each sentence, then listen to the three possible replies. Mark the letter of the reply that best responds to each sentence.

1. (a) (b) (c)

2. (a) (b) (c)

3. (a) (b) (c)

III Speaking

A. You are out shopping at a Chinese clothing store. The shopkeeper is encouraging you to buy this piece of clothing. Do you want to buy it? Why or why not?

B. Your Chinese friend has suggested that you go see a movie together tonight, but you don't want to go. You think the movie your friend has suggested isn't interesting. What will you say to let your friend know that you disagree with his or her suggestion? Make sure to also let your friend know why you disagree!

IV Reading

A. Read the following passage and draw a line from each person to the thing that he or she will buy for the birthday person.

下个星期四是我同学春春的生日。我知道她喜欢看书。我要送她一本有意思的书。文文知道春春喜欢好看的衣服。文文要送她一件好看的衣服。明明知道春春喜欢做运动。明明想送她一个足球。你觉得这个礼物好不好？

1. The writer	**a.** A soccer ball
2. Chunchun	**b.** An interesting book
3. Wenwen	**c.** A nice piece of clothing
4. Mingming	**d.** Nothing—is the birthday person

B. A lot of Daming's stuff is in storage in the U.S., but there are still some items (both clothes and other things) that he needs to pack to take back to college. How many pieces of clothing are on his packing list so far? (Hint: Pay attention to the measure words.) Write the answer in Arabic numerals.

一个本子
两件毛衣
四包方便面
一件外套
三件衬衫
两本书
一副耳机
四件短袖

Pieces of clothing: _____

C. Read the dialogue and mark the statements that follow true (T) or false (F).

Yueyue: 我今天要买一件衣服。你今天要买什么？

Dingding: 我也要买一件衣服。

Yueyue: 你看！这件衣服的颜色很好看。你买这件吧。

Dingding: 可是我觉得这个颜色不好看。

Yueyue: 那你喜欢什么颜色？

Dingding: 我喜欢那个颜色。你看！那件衣服很好看。

Yueyue: 我觉得那件衣服不好看，而且很贵。

Dingding: 那你买这件衣服，我买那件衣服吧！

Yueyue: 好主意。我同意！

	T	F
1. Dingding and Yueyue both want to buy a piece of clothing today.	○	○
2. Yueyue suggests he buy a book instead.	○	○
3. Dingding doesn't like the color of the item Yueyue suggests.	○	○
4. Yueyue thinks the item that Dingding suggests is too expensive.	○	○
5. In the end, Dingding and Yueyue decide not to buy anything.	○	○

V Writing

A. Use the words in the list to complete the dialogue. Use each word only once.

Choices: 不好看，那个，同意，觉得，问，衣服，件，颜色

Chunchun: 明明，我 _____ 你，你觉得那件 _____ 好看吗？

Mingming: 我觉得那件衣服 _____。我不喜欢 _____ 颜色。

Chunchun: 那，这 _____ 呢？这个 _____ 很好看！你买这件吧！

Mingming: 我不 _____。我 _____ 这个颜色也不好看。

Chunchun: 是吗？

B. Translate the following English phrases into Chinese.

1. A very expensive piece of clothing _____

2. A nice-looking guzheng _____

3. An uninteresting book _____

4. A very interesting person _____

Put the Pieces Together!

I Chapter Vocabulary Chart

Fill in the pinyin for and the definition of each word that you learned in this chapter. Use the extra spaces at the end of the chart to add any additional words you learned.

No.	Word	Pinyin	Definition
1	喂		
2	早上		
3	下午		
4	要		
5	晚上		
6	事		
7	见		
8	中午		
9	上午		
10	本		
11	便宜		

No.	Word	Pinyin	Definition
12	难		
13	简单		
14	而且		
15	贵		
16	件		
17	衣服		
18	好看		
19	送		
20	颜色		
21	同意		

II Reading

A. Read the passage and answer the questions that follow.

这个星期五，星期六和星期天我都有事。星期五晚上我要学中文。我也想看书。我有一本中文书。这本书很简单，也很有意思。星期六早上我要去踢足球，下午我要教我弟弟打篮球。星期天上午我要学吉他。中午我要去"欢欢的小店"买一件衣服。那儿的衣服很好看，而且不太贵。星期天晚上我和朋友要去看电影。

1. What is the writer planning to do on Friday night?
   (a) study Chinese and watch a movie
   (b) study Chinese and read a book
   (c) read a book and watch a movie

2. When is the writer going to play soccer?
   (a) Saturday early morning
   (b) Saturday late morning
   (c) Saturday afternoon

3. What does the writer plan to do on Sunday around noon?
   (a) buy an interesting book at"欢欢的小店"
   (b) buy an expensive pet at"欢欢的小店"
   (c) buy a nice-looking, inexpensive piece of clothing at "欢欢的小店"

4. What is the writer planning do on Sunday night, and with whom?
   (a) watch a movie with friends
   (b) watch a movie with his/her younger brother
   (c) watch a movie with his/her parents

III Writing

A. 京京 is having a birthday party this Saturday, so 明明 and 月月 are planning to go shopping for presents. Write a dialogue between them discussing when they will go shopping and what they want to buy. Keep the facts below in mind as you write the dialogue. The first and last lines of the dialogue have been suggested for you.

明明

- Is free tonight and tomorrow evening
- Knows that 京京 likes to read
- Thinks that books are not too expensive

月月

- Is free tomorrow afternoon and evening
- Knows what color clothing 京京 likes
- Doesn't want to buy a very cheap gift

First line

———: 你好！这个星期六是京京的生日。你想送她什么礼物？

Last line

———: 好的！———— 见！

_____

_____

_____

_____

_____

_____

_____

A Birthday Dinner

Can-Do Goals

In this chapter, you are learning to:

- Talk about things you do for others

- Name some Chinese dishes and say what foods you like

- Recognize some Chinese holiday foods

- Order food from a restaurant

- Discuss completed actions

- State opinions and give reasons

Doing things for others

Audio

I   Pinyin and Tone

A. The word 菜 (cài) begins with the c- initial sound. Listen to the recording and complete the pinyin for only the words that begin with the c- initial sound.

1. ___ài   **2.** ___uò   **3.** ___ǎng   **4.** ___ì   **5.** ___ā   **6.** ___ān

Audio

II   Listening

A. Listen as the speaker says how she feels about the various items pictured below. Write the letter of the picture that matches each statement. (Each picture will be described only once.)

1. ___   **2.** ___   **3.** ___   **4.** ___

a

b

中文

c

d

B. You will hear a statement followed by three possible responses. Choose the letter of the response that best corresponds to each statement.

1. (a) (b) (c)

2. (a) (b) (c)

3. (a) (b) (c)

4. (a) (b) (c)

III Speaking

A. Imagine that a Chinese exchange student your school hosted earlier in the year has gone back to China, but you've kept in touch. How would you suggest that you call him next Wednesday evening?

B. Your Chinese friend is buying a cake for the class. She sends you a picture of this cake to see what you think. Do you think it is nice-looking? Do you think it will be tasty? Give your answer using complete Chinese sentences.

IV Reading

A. Although this kind of booth is less common in Shanghai nowadays, some people might still find it handy. Refer to the Chinese writing in the picture. Besides using WiFi, what else can you do there? Give your answer in English.

B. Read the dialogue, then choose the option that correctly completes each statement.

Younger brother: 哥哥，妈妈不在家，她今天晚上有事。

Older brother: 我知道。爸爸今天也不在家。那我们打电话点菜吧！

Younger brother: 可是我今天想在家做菜。我想给你做一种好吃的菜。

Older brother: 好啊。可是你会做菜吗？

Younger brother: 我会做菜。你看！你喜欢吃这种菜吗？

Older brother: 喜欢，这种菜很好吃。

1. The brothers' parents will not eat at home tonight because
   (a) they are going to a restaurant without their sons.
   (b) the mother has something to do and the father won't be home.
   (c) the mother is out of the country and the father has things to do.

2. The younger brother doesn't want his older brother to order food tonight because
   (a) he doesn't like the restaurant his brother likes.
   (b) he doesn't like the food his brother wants to order.
   (c) he wants to make food at home.

3. The older brother is unsure that
   (a) his younger brother knows the restaurant well.
   (b) his younger brother can cook.
   (c) his younger brother has ever eaten dumplings before.

4. The younger brother offers to
   (a) make a dish that his older brother thinks is tasty.
   (b) buy food from a different restaurant.
   (c) make the call to order food.

5. When the younger brother says "你看！" he is likely showing his brother
   (a) the phone number for the restaurant.
   (b) a picture of food in a cookbook.
   (c) a picture of their parents.

V | Writing

A. Complete the sentences as indicated by the emojis.

1. 我觉得 _____

2. 欢欢觉得 _____

3. 我爸爸觉得 _____

4. 你觉得 _____ 吗?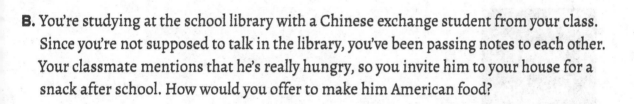

B. You're studying at the school library with a Chinese exchange student from your class. Since you're not supposed to talk in the library, you've been passing notes to each other. Your classmate mentions that he's really hungry, so you invite him to your house for a snack after school. How would you offer to make him American food?

_____

Talking about yesterday

I Pinyin and Tone

A. Match each picture with the pinyin for the word in Chinese.

1.

       a. fànguǎn

2.

       b. miàntiáo

3.

       c. hóngshāo ròu

4.

       d. jiǎozi

5.

       e. cài

II Listening

A. Listen to the dialogue and mark the following statements true (T) or false (F).

	T	F
1. The man suggests that they go to a restaurant.	○	○
2. The woman says she wants to eat noodles.	○	○
3. The man wants to eat red-cooked pork.	○	○
4. The man offers to order food for the woman.	○	○

B. Listen to the recording of three people talking about things they did yesterday. Write the number of the statement next to the picture of the activity that is mentioned in the recording.

C. Martin has gotten lost in his neighborhood, so he calls Daming for help. Listen to their conversation, then select the image that best represents where Martin is right now.

III Speaking

A. Your Chinese friend asks you if you ate Chinese food yesterday. How do you respond?

B. Imagine that you want to call your local Chinese restaurant and order food using Chinese. How would you begin your call and what would you order?

A. Imagine that you are walking around Beijing and come across these two restaurants. Based on the signs, what is something you could order from Restaurant 1? What could you order from Restaurant 2? Which characters do you see that lead you to that conclusion?

B. Below are four questions, each followed by three possible answers. Choose the statement that best answers each question.

1. 你点了几份面条?

   (a) 我点了三份饺子。

   (b) 我明天要吃一份面条。

   (c) 我点了两份面条。

2. 昨天你做了什么菜?

   (a) 昨天我做了红烧肉。

   (b) 昨天我做了两个菜。

   (c) 昨天我吃了面条。

3. 饺子好吃吗?

   (a) 饺子很好吃。

   (b) 我吃了饺子。

   (c) 我不想吃饺子。

4. 你吃了吗?

   (a) 我去了饭馆。

   (b) 我吃了。

   (c) 我喜欢吃饺子。

Ⅴ Writing

A. Rearrange the Chinese words given to create correct sentences. The first word of each sentence has been provided for you.

1. 你 _____

吃了 ┆ 昨天 ┆ 吗? ┆ 面条

2. 我 _____

饺子。 ┆ 吃 ┆ 没有 ┆ 昨天

3. 谁 _____

做 ┆ 昨天 ┆ 菜了?

4. 我 _____

一份 ┆ 吃了 ┆ 昨天 ┆ 菜。 ┆ 好吃的

B. Complete the dialogue using the words in the list. You will use one word twice!

Choices: 了，做，昨天，面条，饭馆，红烧肉

 你今天想不想吃 _____?

 不想。我 _____ 吃 _____ 面条。

 那，你今天想吃什么? 想不想去 _____ 吃?

 我不想去饭馆。我想在家吃 _____。

 你家有红烧肉吗?

 有。妈妈昨天晚上教我 _____ 红烧肉 _____。

Asking and answering the question "why?"

I Pinyin and Tone

Audio

A. Listen to the recording and write the pinyin for each word you hear. Make sure to mark the tone. You may write the tone mark above the vowel or write the number of the tone after the word.

1. _____ 2. _____ 3. _____ 4. _____ 5. _____ 6. _____

II Listening

Audio

A. Listen to the dialogue and mark the following statements true (T) or false (F).

        T **F**

1. It is the man's birthday. ◯ ◯

2. The woman is giving someone else a birthday present. ◯ ◯

3. The woman wants to wish someone a happy birthday. ◯ ◯

B. Listen to the woman talk about her favorite neighborhood restaurant, then answer the questions.

1. When did the speaker go to the restaurant?
   (a) yesterday for dinner
   (b) yesterday for lunch
   (c) yesterday, but she doesn't say what time of day

2. Why does the speaker frequently go to this restaurant?
   (a) because the food is inexpensive
   (b) because she thinks there is a lot of delicious food there
   (c) because her friends also really like it

III Speaking

A. Your Chinese friend's parents have offered to make you a dish of Chinese food! They've given you two options to choose from, a or b. Which do you want to eat, and why? Remember to use 因为 and 所以 in your response!

B. You've learned how to wish someone a happy birthday in Chinese. In Chinese, the common word for "holiday" is 节日 (jiérì). How would you wish someone a happy holiday in Chinese?

IV Reading

A. Wenwen and her mother share a birthday. Read the sentences below and number them in the correct order to create a logical conversation.

___ **Mother:** 文文，也祝你生日快乐！

___ **Wenwen:** 妈妈，祝你生日快乐！

___ **Wenwen:** 我要送你一个礼物。你看！因为你是音乐老师，所以我送你一本音乐书。

___ **Mother:** 谢谢你，文文。妈妈也要送你一个礼物。你看，这是什么？

___ **Mother:** 因为我知道你很喜欢猫，所以我给你买了这只猫。

___ **Wenwen:** 一只猫！

___ **Wenwen:** 谢谢妈妈！

B. Read the passage, then choose the option that correctly completes each statement.

今天是我的生日。爸爸知道我喜欢音乐，所以他给我买了一个吉他。妈妈知道我喜欢什么颜色，所以她给我买了一件好看的衣服。我有很多好朋友。他们也送了我很多礼物。因为我喜欢运动，所以他们送了我一个足球和一个篮球。我很喜欢我的生日礼物！

1. The writer's father bought him a guitar because
   (a) he knows the writer has always wanted a guitar.
   (b) he knows the writer likes music.
   (c) he knows the writer can play guitar well.

2. The writer's mother bought him a nice piece of clothing because
   (a) she knows what color he likes.
   (b) she knows he doesn't have a lot of clothing.
   (c) she knows where to buy nice, inexpensive clothing.

3. The writer's many friends bought him a soccer ball and a basketball because
   (a) they know he wants to exercise more.
   (b) they know he lost his other basketball and soccer ball.
   (c) they know he likes playing sports and exercising.

4. The writer says that he
   (a) really likes his birthday presents.
   (b) doesn't really like his birthday presents.
   (c) thinks all of his birthday presents are boring.

C. Sanjay has just met Maya's new dog. Read Sanjay and Maya's conversation and mark the statements that follow true (T) or false (F).

Maya，这是你的狗吗？

是啊。

它叫什么名字？

它叫小白。

下个月我们小区在网球场有一个宠物比赛。小白可以去。

可是，下个月二十号我要去美国。

比赛是六月五号。

六月五号是星期几？

星期四。

好。那我和小白可以去！

那我们六月五号见。小白加油啊！

好啊。小白加油啊！

	T	F
1. Maya's dog's name is Xiaobai.	○	○
2. Sanjay tells Maya about a pet competition at their school.	○	○
3. Maya is going to America after the pet competition.	○	○
4. The pet competition will take place over the weekend.	○	○
5. Maya seems excited to take her dog to the pet competition.	○	○

V Writing

A. Use the words and phrases in the list to complete the dialogue. You will use some twice!

Choices: 因为，所以，为什么，我不想去，很多

A: 我很想去这个饭馆。_____ 这个饭馆的菜都很便宜，_____ 我喜欢。你想不想去这个饭馆？

B: 不想。

A: _____ ?

B: 因为我觉得这个饭馆的菜不好吃，所以_____。我们在我家吃吧！我可以给你做_____ 好吃的菜。

A: 好啊！_____ 你很会做菜，_____ 我很想吃！

B. Answer the following questions based on your own preferences using 因为 ... 所以 ...

1. 你想买这件衣服吗？

_____

$12

2. 你想吃这个菜吗？

_____

Put the Pieces Together!

I Chapter Vocabulary Chart

Fill in the pinyin for and the definition of each word that you learned in this chapter. Use the extra spaces at the end of the chart to add any additional words you learned.

No.	Word	Pinyin	Definition
1	吃		
2	好吃		
3	菜		
4	种		
5	点		
6	给		
7	打电话		
8	做菜		
9	饺子		
10	昨天		
11	了		

No.	Word	Pinyin	Definition
12	饭馆		
13	份		
14	面条		
15	红烧		
16	肉		
17	祝		
18	快乐		
19	为什么		
20	因为		
21	所以		
22	多		

II Reading

A. Read the passage and then answer the questions below.

昨天晚上，我和爸爸、妈妈去了朋朋饭馆。我们点了很多菜。我点了红烧肉。爸爸点了饺子。妈妈喜欢吃面条，所以我们给她点了一份面条。因为这个饭馆的菜很好吃，而且不贵，所以很多人喜欢这个饭馆。我的朋友文文和她的爸爸、妈妈昨天也去了这个饭馆。他们也点了面条。为什么呢？因为昨天是文文的生日。

1. Which of the following statements is NOT true?

   (a) The writer ordered red-cooked pork.
   (b) The writer's mother ordered noodles.
   (c) The writer's family ordered a lot of dishes.

2. Which of the following statements is NOT true?
   (a) The food at Pengpeng's Restaurant is tasty.
   (b) The prices at Pengpeng's Restaurant are expensive.
   (c) Many people like Pengpeng's Restaurant.

3. Only ONE of the following statements is true. Which is it?
   (a) The writer's friend Wenwen and her family also went to Pengpeng's Restaurant last night.
   (b) The writer's friend Wenwen and her family also went to a restaurant last night, but it was not Pengpeng's Restaurant.
   (c) Today is Wenwen's birthday, so she will go to Pengpeng's Restaurant with her family tonight.

4. Only ONE of the following statements is true. Which is it?
   (a) Wenwen and her family ordered noodles for dinner.
   (b) Wenwen's family includes a mother, a father, and an older brother.
   (c) The writer and everyone else wished Wenwen a happy birthday.

A. Look at this photo of a family birthday celebration. Imagine that it happened yesterday and that you were one of the people at the party. Write a short note telling a Chinese friend about the event. Describe what you ate and your opinion of what you ate. The Chinese word for cake is 蛋糕 (dàngāo). You can also make up other details about the party that aren't shown in the photo. Use a dictionary to look up any other words you might want to include in your description!

_____

_____

_____

_____

Too Many Classes!

Can-Do Goals

In this chapter, you are learning to:

- Understand the Chinese school system and compare it to your own

- Talk about your favorite classes

- Compare and contrast different things

- Tell someone what you are about to do

- Express both strong and weak opinions

- Describe someone's feelings

Class preferences

Audio

I Pinyin and Tone

A. The sounds of the word 学 are represented by the pinyin "xue." Listen to the recording and place a check on the line provided for each word that is pronounced "xue." For this exercise, you do not need to pay attention to the tone. The first question has been done for you.

1. ✓   2. ____   3. ____   4. ____   5. ____

B. Listen to the recording and mark the tone for each word. You may write the tone mark above the pinyin provided, or write the number of the tone beside the word.

1. 最 zui   2. 哪 na   3. 门 men   4. 课 ke   5. 还 hai

Audio

II Listening

A. Listen to the dialogue and mark the following statements true (T) or false (F).

	T	F
1. The speaker does not like Chinese class.	○	○
2. The speaker likes science class.	○	○
3. The speaker likes math class the best.	○	○
4. The speaker thinks math is difficult.	○	○

B. Listen to the dialogue and answer the following questions.

1. Which of the following questions does the boy ask the girl?
   (a) Do you like Chinese class?
   (b) What is your favorite class?
   (c) Do you like math class?

2. Which of the following statements is true?
   (a) The girl and the boy both like Chinese class.
   (b) The girl and the boy both like math class.
   (c) Neither the girl nor the boy likes math class.

III Speaking

A. Look at the pictures representing different classes and talk about your favorites.

IV Reading

A. Read the dialogue and mark the statements that follow true (T) or false (F).

 你觉得哪门课最有意思？

 因为我喜欢科学，所以我觉得科学课最有意思。你呢？

 我也喜欢科学，可是我觉得科学课很难。我觉得中文最有意思，而且不太难，所以我最喜欢中文课。我还喜欢音乐课和数学课。

	T	F
1. Maya likes science class the best because she is interested in science.	◯	◯
2. Owen likes science class because it is easy.	◯	◯
3. Owen likes Chinese class but thinks that it is very hard.	◯	◯
4. Owen does not like music class.	◯	◯

B. Read the dialogue and mark the statements that follow true (T) or false (F).

 你最喜欢哪种运动？

 我最喜欢打篮球。你呢？你喜欢哪种运动？

 我也很喜欢打篮球。我还喜欢打网球。

 我不太会打网球，可是我想学网球。我还想学乒乓球。

	T	F
1. Miko's favorite sport is ping-pong.	○	○
2. Ellen likes to play basketball and tennis.	○	○
3. Miko can play tennis very well.	○	○

C. Match each Chinese textbook below to the letter of its subject.

1

2

3

4

a. math   b. science   c. Chinese history   d. music

V Writing

A. Rearrange the Chinese words and phrases to create logical sentences.

1. _____

哪门｜最｜你｜课?｜喜欢

2. _____

最｜课｜她｜觉得｜数学｜有意思。

3. _____

还｜课。｜科学｜喜欢｜我

4. _____

踢足球。｜要｜他明天｜还｜去

B. Use the words in the list to complete the dialogue. Use each word only once.

Choices: 那，哪，还，也，最，觉得，想

 你 ___ 喜欢 ___ 个饭馆?

 我最喜欢"快乐饭馆"。___ 个饭馆的饺子很好吃。

 我 ___ 喜欢吃饺子。那我们明天去"快乐饭馆"吃饺子吧!

 好啊! 你 ___ 想点什么菜?

 我还 ___ 点红烧肉。

 太好了。我也 ___ 红烧肉很好吃!

Choosing courses

Audio

I Pinyin and Tone

A. Listen to the recording. You will hear several words that use the final sound "uo." Fill in the blank with the correct initial sound. The first five words you will hear are all words you have already learned, but the bonus word is one that you will learn in Chapter 14!

1. 说 __ uō **2.** 所 __ uǒ **3.** 多 __ uō **4.** 做 __ uò **5.** 昨 __ uó

Bonus: 错 __ uò

Audio

II Listening

A. Listen as the speaker talks about the various subjects she is learning. Write the letter of the picture that matches the subject she mentions in each statement. (Each picture will be described only once.)

1. ___ 2. ___ 3. ___ 4. ___

a — Chinese b — American literature c — American history d — math

B. Listen to the dialogue and mark the following statements true (T) or false (F).

T　F

1. The girl asks the boy where he's going tomorrow. ◯ ◯
2. The boy is about to go to his friend's house to watch a movie. ◯ ◯
3. The girl says she thinks science is very important. ◯ ◯
4. The girl is about to go to a basketball court. ◯ ◯
5. The boy says he thinks reading is more important than exercising. ◯ ◯

III Speaking

A. Do you like math or history better? Which do you think is more interesting? More important? Easier to study? Use 比 to express your opinions.

B. Imagine that it's Saturday morning and you are talking to a friend on the phone. It's time for you to do the next thing on your schedule, so use 要 … 了 to describe what you are about to do and then say goodbye.

IV Reading

A. Chunchun has received an email from her friend asking for advice on choosing classes. Read the email and mark the statements that follow true (T) or false (F).

春春，我不知道要选什么课。我知道历史和文学都很重要。可是月月说历史更重要，明明说文学更重要。你觉得历史比文学重要吗？你选了什么课？

	T	F
1. The writer thinks that history and literature are both important subjects.	○	○
2. The writer's friend Yueyue thinks literature is more important than history.	○	○
3. The writer's friend Mingming says history is more difficult to study.	○	○
4. The writer asks Chunchun which classes she thinks are most interesting.	○	○

B. Read the dialogue below, then choose the option that correctly completes each statement.

大文，今天是星期六。我们下午去看电影吧！你觉得美国电影更好看还是中国电影更好看？

我觉得中国电影比美国电影好看。可是，我现在要去上课了。我下午有笛子课。我们明天去吧？

好啊，上课比看电影更重要。

	T	F
1. Miko suggests that she and Owen should go to a movie this afternoon.	○	○
2. Owen is about to go to class.	○	○
3. Miko says that going to class is more important than watching movies.	○	○

V Writing

A. Use the phrases in the list to complete the dialogue. Use each phrase only once.

Choices: 选一门，更有意思，要选课了，哪门，
中国文学比美国文学

Li Ming: 我们 _____ ！你想选什么课？

Bai Ying: 我想 _____ 文学课。我觉得文学很
有意思。

Li Ming: 你想学 _____ 文学课？中国文学
还是美国文学？

Bai Ying: 我觉得 _____ 有意思，所以我
想学中国文学。你呢？

Li Ming: 我不知道哪门课 _____，可是我朋友
说美国文学课比中国文学课更简单。所以我
想选美国文学课！

B. Between science and history, which class do you think is more important, and which class do you think is more difficult? If you had to pick just one, which class would you choose to take? Write your answer in complete Chinese sentences.

_____

_____

_____

_____

Talking about feelings

I Pinyin and Tone

Audio

A. In many three-character Chinese words and phrases, one of the characters will be read with a neutral tone. Listen to the recording and circle the character in each word or phrase that is read with a neutral tone. The first one has been done for you.

1. 怎么样 (zenmeyang)

2. 为什么 (weishenme)

3. 有意思 (youyisi)

4. 对不起 (duibuqi)

II Listening

Audio

A. Listen as the speaker talks about how he feels. Write the letter of the emoji that matches the feelings he describes in each statement.

1. _____   2. _____   3. _____   4. _____

a   b   c   d

B. Listen to each question, then listen to the three possible answers. Mark the letter of the statement that best answers each question.

1. (a) (b) (c)

2. (a) (b) (c)

3. (a) (b) (c)

III Speaking

A. Describe how you think the people in the photos are feeling and why.

B. Imagine that your Chinese friend has just asked how you're doing today. How will you respond?

IV Reading

A. Read the dialogue and mark the statements that follow true (T) or false (F).

Student:	我想学一种中国乐器。李老师，你觉得怎么样？
Mr. Li:	我觉得挺好的啊！你想选二胡还是古筝？我都可以教你。
Student:	太好了！可是我不知道选哪个……李老师，你喜欢二胡还是古筝？
Mr. Li:	我都挺喜欢的，可是我觉得古筝比二胡更好听。
Student:	那我选古筝吧！
Mr. Li:	好啊。

T F

1. Guzheng is the only Chinese musical instrument Mr. Li can teach. ○ ○

2. Mr. Li prefers erhu to guzheng. ○ ○

3. The student decides to learn guzheng. ○ ○

B. Read the dialogue and answer the questions that follow.

 我今天心情不太好。

 为什么?

 我也不知道。

 那我们去宠物店吧，怎么样? 我知道你挺喜欢宠物的。

 太好了! 那我们现在去吧?

 好啊。那你现在的心情怎么样?

 我现在挺高兴的。

1. How is Owen feeling at the beginning of the conversation?
   (a) He isn't very happy because he thinks history class is hard.
   (b) He isn't very happy, but he doesn't know why.
   (c) He's in a great mood today.

2. What does Leo suggest?
   (a) He suggests Owen study harder.
   (b) He suggests they go clothes shopping.
   (c) He suggests they go to a pet store.

3. How does Owen react to Leo's suggestion?
   (a) He thinks it's a bad idea.
   (b) He wants to go right away.
   (c) He thinks it's a good idea but wants to do it tomorrow.

4. How is Owen feeling at the end of the conversation?
   (a) He's pretty happy.
   (b) He's so happy he can barely contain himself.
   (c) He's not in a great mood.

V Writing

A. Rearrange the Chinese words and phrases to create logical sentences.

1. _____

怎么样？ │ 心情 │ 你这个周末

2. _____

太 │ 重要 │ 历史课 │ 觉得 │ 我 │ 了！

3. _____

便宜 │ 挺 │ 衣服 │ 这件 │ 的。

4. _____

的。 │ 紧张 │ 挺 │ 现在 │ 她

B. Describe the type of store these people are in, and what their moods seem to be.

_____

_____

Put the Pieces Together!

I Chapter Vocabulary Chart

Fill in the pinyin for and the definition of each word that you learned in this chapter. Use the extra spaces at the end of the chart to add any additional words you learned.

No.	Word	Pinyin	Definition
1	最		
2	哪		
3	门		
4	课		
5	科学		
6	还		
7	数学		
8	选		
9	历史		
10	文学		
11	说		

No.	Word	Pinyin	Definition
12	比		
13	更		
14	重要		
15	上课		
16	心情		
17	怎么样		
18	挺		
19	高兴		
20	太		
21	紧张		

A. Read the dialogue below and mark the statements that follow true (T) or false (F).

Mingming: 你现在要去哪儿？

Tiantian: 我要去书店买书了。……你心情不太好吗？

Mingming: 是啊。下个星期是文文的生日，可是我不知道送什么礼物给她。

Tiantian: 你知道她最喜欢哪门课吗？

Mingming: 她说她最喜欢历史课。她还挺喜欢数学课的。

Tiantian: 那你送她一本历史书，怎么样？

Mingming: 这个主意太好了。
（在书店……）

Tiantian: 你看，这本历史书和那本历史书怎么样？我觉得都挺好的。

Mingming: 我觉得这本书比那本书更有意思，而且更便宜。我选这本书吧。太谢谢你了！

	T	F
1. Tiantian is about to go to the bookstore.	○	○
2. Mingming wants to give Wenwen a birthday gift.	○	○
3. Tiantian knows which class Wenwen likes best.	○	○
4. Wenwen likes history class best.	○	○
5. Mingming chooses the more interesting and expensive book to give to Wenwen.	○	○

A. Here is a description of the activities Leo did this weekend and how he felt while doing them. Imagine that you are Leo, writing your diary entries on Sunday night about the weekend. The first lines of the diary have been suggested for you.

	Activity	心情
星期五	同学的生日 去饭馆吃饭	高兴
星期六	看乒乓球比赛： 我们学校 vs. 北京明兴学校	紧张
	和朋友看电影	高兴
星期天	想买一件很好看的衣服 那件衣服太贵了	不太高兴

这个星期五是我同学的生日，我们去饭馆吃中国菜了
中国菜很好吃，所以我们这个星期五都挺高兴的！

_____

_____

_____

_____

How's It Going?

Can-Do Goals   **In this chapter, you are learning to:**

- Discuss the specific time of an activity or event

- Understand when others talk about running later than expected

- Talk about what you need to do every day or every week

- Talk about doing things with other people

- Express how you are the same as or different from someone else

- Understand aspects of student life in China and compare to your own experience

Talking about time

Audio

I   Pinyin and Tone

A. Listen to the recording and complete the pinyin for each word with either c, q, or ch. (Reminder: you know the c initial sound from 菜, the q initial sound from 七, and the ch initial sound from 吃.)

1. ____ ái   **2.** ____ ǐ   **3.** ____ uáng   **4.** ____ uī   **5.** ____ uò   **6.** ____ íng

Audio

II   Listening

A. Listen to the dialogue and mark the following statements true (T) or false (F).

	T	F
1. The boy didn't go to sleep until 11:30 last night.	◯	◯
2. The boy went to sleep late last night because his math homework was too hard.	◯	◯
3. The boy and the girl agreed that there was a lot of homework yesterday.	◯	◯
4. The girl didn't go to sleep until 11:00 last night.	◯	◯

B. Listen to the passage and mark the following statements true (T) or false (F).

	T	F
1. The speaker got up at 8:10 this morning.	◯	◯
2. The speaker didn't start doing his homework until 9:30 last night.	◯	◯
3. The speaker seems to think he went to bed too late last night.	◯	◯
4. Today, the speaker intends to start doing his homework earlier and go to bed earlier.	◯	◯

III   Speaking

A. Talk about what time you wake up in the morning and what time your classes start.

B. Imagine that you overslept this morning. How would you tell your classmates about what happened? Hint: try using 才 to express that you woke up later than you should have.

IV Reading

A. Read the dialogue and mark the statements that follow true (T) or false (F).

Mother: 你知道现在是几点吗？

Son: 九点半啊。

Mother: 对啊。那你现在才开始做作业，你想几点睡觉？

Son: 今天的作业不多。我想十点十分去睡觉。

Mother: 好吧。我们明天早上有事儿。你明天可以六点半起床吗？

Son: 可以。

	T	F
1. The boy says the current time is 9:00 p.m.	○	○
2. The mother thinks the boy has started doing his homework too late.	○	○
3. The boy doesn't have much homework, so he doesn't think he'll go to sleep too late.	○	○
4. The mother asks the boy if he wants to eat breakfast at 6:30 tomorrow morning.	○	○

B. Read Mingming's email about his weekend schedule and mark the statements that follow true (T) or false (F).

昨天是星期六。我上午八点十五分起床，十点开始做数学作业。数学作业挺难的，而且很多。下午两点半我开始做历史作业。历史作业比数学作业更多！晚上我还做了科学和文学作业，十一点半才睡觉。今天我没有作业，我可以十点起床。我还可以去打篮球和看电影。你呢？你这个周末忙不忙？

	T	F
1. Mingming didn't start doing his homework until 2:30 p.m. on Saturday.	○	○
2. Mingming says he had more homework for history than for math.	○	○
3. Mingming went to bed at 10:30 p.m. on Saturday.	○	○
4. On Sunday, Mingming plans to play basketball and see a movie.	○	○

A. Use Chinese characters to write the time shown on each clock.

1. _____

2. _____

3. _____

4. _____

5. _____

B. Re-read the email from Mingming about his weekend schedule. At the end of the email he asks you about your weekend. Use the lines below to respond to his question and also tell him a bit about your weekend plans. (You can discuss your real plans or imaginary plans.)

_____

_____

_____

Talking about schedules

I Pinyin and Tone

Audio

A. Listen to the recording and circle every character that is read in the second tone. The first one has been done for you.

1. (时)间   2. 累   3. 忙   4. 分

5. 才   6. 点   7. 不用   8. 起床

II Listening

Audio

A. Listen to each sentence, then listen to the three possible responses. Mark the letter of the statement that best responds to each sentence.

1. (a) (b) (c)

2. (a) (b) (c)

3. (a) (b) (c)

4. (a) (b) (c)

B. Listen to the girl talk about her day and look at the images below. Write the letters of the images in the order that the girl mentions them.

III Speaking

A. Look at this student's schedule for the week. Today is Monday. Say one thing he has to do every day and one thing he doesn't have to do today.

星期一	星期二	星期三	星期四	星期五
学中文 弹吉他	看历史书 学中文	学中文 去踢足球	看科学书 学中文 上二胡课 教弟弟中文	学中文 弹吉他

B. Look at the student's schedule in Speaking exercise A again. On which day is this student busiest? Describe his activities on that day.

IV Reading

A. Read the dialogue and mark the statements that follow true (T) or false (F).

Student A: 你今天心情不好吗？

Student B: 是啊！昨天科学课的作业太难了。我十一点才睡觉……我太累了！为什么我们每天都得上科学课啊……

Student A: 我也觉得昨天的科学作业很多。可是我挺喜欢学科学的，所以我不觉得累。

		T	F
1.	Both students have to take science class.	○	○
2.	Both students say there is a lot of science homework, but it's not too hard.	○	○
3.	Both students say they feel tired.	○	○
4.	Both students seem to like science class.	○	○

B. Read the dialogue and mark the statements that follow true (T) or false (F).

Younger brother:	哥哥，你现在有时间吗？我想去打篮球，你去吗？
Older brother:	我现在很忙，没有时间。
Younger brother:	你每天都说你很忙……
Older brother:	对啊。我每天都有很多课，晚上还得做很多作业。你不用做作业吗？
Younger brother:	我也得做作业。可是妈妈说，做作业很重要，做运动也很重要啊！
Older brother:	对，做运动也很重要。那我们现在去打篮球吧！

              T **F**

1. The younger brother wants to tell his older brother about his classes. ◯ ◯

2. The older brother has to take many classes and do a lot of homework every day. ◯ ◯

3. The younger brother doesn't need to do homework. ◯ ◯

4. Their mother said that doing homework is more important than playing sports. ◯ ◯

5. In the end, the two brothers go play basketball together. ◯ ◯

V Writing

A. Write a complete Chinese sentence using the 每 … 都 structure to describe each photo. Hint: some useful words that can be used are 贵, 忙, and 累.

_____

B. Use the words and phrases in the list to complete the passage.

Choices: 得，每个，累，都，忙，不用，没有时间，
可以，做作业

昨天是星期五。我 _____ 星期五 _____
很 _____！我 _____ 上课和做运动，
还得弹古筝和 _____。可是昨天妈妈说，
"你 _____ 今天晚上做作业，你 _____
周末做作业。"所以昨天晚上我和朋友去看电影了，
我 _____ 做作业。昨天我很高兴，可是今天
我觉得太 _____ 了！

Shared experiences

I Pinyin and Tone

Audio

A. When the character 一 is the first character in a word, its tone changes based on the tone of the second character. Listen to the recording and use the lines given below to indicate in which words 一 has a second tone and in which words 一 has a fourth tone.

a. 一起 (together)

b. 一样 (same)

c. 一定 (definitely)

d. 一下 (once; quickly)

e. 一种 (one type of)

f. 一同 (in unison)

yí: _____

yì: _____

II Listening

Audio

A. Listen to the dialogue and answer the following questions.

1. What does the girl do on weekends?
  (a) She listens to music every weekend.
  (b) She sometimes listens to music and sometimes watches movies.
  (c) She sometimes plays the guitar and sometimes watches TV.

2. What does the boy like to do?
  (a) He likes to watch movies.
  (b) He likes to listen to music.
  (c) He does not like to watch movies or listen to music.

3. What will the boy and girl do next week?
  (a) They will listen to music together.
  (b) They will see a movie together.
  (c) They will play sports together.

B. Listen to each question, then listen to the three possible answers. Mark the letter of the statement that best answers each question.

1. (a) (b) (c)

2. (a) (b) (c)

3. (a) (b) (c)

C. This passage helps you review what you learned in earlier chapters. Listen to the dialogue and answer the following questions.

1. The woman asks the man if he knows
   (a) where the basketball court is.
   (b) where the soccer field is.
   (c) where she can go to buy books.

2. The man suggests that
   (a) they go to the basketball court together.
   (b) the woman watch his basketball game.
   (c) the woman learn how to play soccer.

3. The man tells the woman that
   (a) he thinks basketball is more interesting than soccer.
   (b) he thinks that soccer and basketball are equally interesting.
   (c) he teaches basketball.

III Speaking

A. In complete Chinese sentences, describe something that you did with someone else today. (Reminder: Use 跟.) What time did you do this thing? Give other details if you can.

B. Use complete Chinese sentences to describe each photo. Try to use the word 一样 in your descriptions.

IV Reading

A. Read the dialogue and mark the statements that follow true (T) or false (F).

 你今天晚上有时间吗？我们一起去饭馆吃饭吧！

 我每天晚上都要去音乐学校上课，没有时间啊。

 你在音乐学校学什么？

 学中国乐器。我很喜欢中国音乐，所以我学了两种中国乐器。我有的时候拉二胡，有的时候弹古筝。

 我跟你一样，我也很喜欢古筝，可是我不会弹古筝。我可以跟你一起去吗？我想听你弹古筝。

可以啊。

	T	F
1. Miko goes to the music school every afternoon.	○	○
2. Miko has free time tonight.	○	○
3. Miko says she is learning the erhu because her father said that she has to.	○	○
4. Miko sometimes plays the erhu and sometimes plays the guzheng.	○	○
5. Both Miko and Owen like guzheng.	○	○

B. The person advertising wants to create an English version of his poster. How would you translate the main message of the poster (shown in the largest characters) into English?

跟林老师
一起学英文！

每个星期二、四 17:00 见面
有问题？给我打电话: XXX . XXXX . XXXX

电子邮件: llaoshi@email

_____

_____

V Writing

A. Complete the translation of the sentences.

1. 你要 ＿＿＿＿＿＿＿ 我一起 ＿＿＿＿＿＿＿ 吗？

   Do you want to listen to music with me?

2. 这个饭馆的菜 ＿＿＿＿＿＿ 那个饭馆的菜 ＿＿＿＿＿＿＿。

   The dishes at this restaurant are as expensive as the ones at that restaurant.

3. 我 ＿＿＿＿＿＿＿，我也 ＿＿＿＿＿＿＿＿＿＿。

   I'm the same as you; I also bought that book.

4. 有的时候我喜欢 ＿＿＿＿＿＿＿＿＿ 看电影，＿＿＿＿＿＿ 我喜欢一个人 ＿＿＿＿＿＿。

   Sometimes I like watching movies together with friends; sometimes I like watching movies alone.

B. Use complete Chinese sentences to give your responses to the prompts below.

1. Write a sentence stating two activities that you find equally interesting.

   ＿＿＿＿＿＿＿＿＿＿＿＿＿＿＿＿＿＿＿＿＿＿＿＿＿＿＿

   ＿＿＿＿＿＿＿＿＿＿＿＿＿＿＿＿＿＿＿＿＿＿＿＿＿＿＿

2. Describe who you do those activities with.

   ＿＿＿＿＿＿＿＿＿＿＿＿＿＿＿＿＿＿＿＿＿＿＿＿＿＿＿

   ＿＿＿＿＿＿＿＿＿＿＿＿＿＿＿＿＿＿＿＿＿＿＿＿＿＿＿

Put the Pieces Together!

I Chapter Vocabulary Chart

Fill in the pinyin for and the definition of each word that you learned in this chapter. Use the extra spaces at the end of the chart to add any additional words you learned.

No.	Word	Pinyin	Definition
1	点		
2	分		
3	才		
4	开始		
5	作业		
6	半		
7	睡觉		
8	起床		
9	时间		
10	忙		
11	每		

No.	Word	Pinyin	Definition
12	天		
13	不用		
14	得		
15	累		
16	有的		
17	时候		
18	跟		
19	一样		
20	一起		
21	饭		
22	已经		

A. In the fictional passage below, a Chinese girl in elementary school describes her schedule and that of her sister in high school. Read the passage and mark the statements that follow true (T) or false (F).

我跟我姐姐一样，我们都是学生。我们每天早上六点半起床，七点吃饭，七点二十分去学校，八点开始上课。我姐姐选了七门课，她每天都得做很多作业。所以她比我忙，也比我累。她经常晚上十一点才睡觉。我跟她不一样，我的课不太多。我每天都有时间去做运动。有的时候，我姐姐也跟我一起做运动。

	T	F
1. The sisters start class at 7:25 every morning.	○	○
2. Both sisters have to do a lot of homework every day.	○	○
3. The older sister is busier than the younger sister.	○	○
4. The older sister often stays up until 11:00 p.m.	○	○
5. The sisters play basketball together every day.	○	○

III Writing

A. Think of someone you know, such as a sibling, classmate, or friend. Write a short paragraph describing three ways you are similar to or different from that person.

_____

_____

_____

Taking Care of Yourself

Can-Do Goals

In this chapter, you are learning to:

- Understand what Chinese students might do to stay healthy
- Talk about what you can do and what the situation allows you to do
- Discuss adjusting plans to do something a bit earlier or later
- Understand when others say they are hungry, thirsty, hot, or cold
- Talk about common health problems
- Express what you do (and do not do) when you are sick

Just a little bit

Audio

I Pinyin and Tone

A. Are the following words second tone or third tone? Listen to the audio and write the tone number of each character on the line provided.

1. 能 ___   2. 水 ___   3. 早 ___   4. 忙 ___   5. 门 ___   6. 晚 ___

Audio

II Listening

A. Listen as the speaker talks about what he/she wants to do, then write the letter of the image that matches each sentence you hear.

1. ____   2. ____   3. ____   4. ____   5. ____   6. ____

B. Listen to the dialogue and answer the questions that follow.

1. What does the boy want to do tomorrow?
   (a) take a day off
   (b) go to a friend's house
   (c) go to school a bit later than usual

2. What does his mom ask him to do tomorrow?
   (a) wake up earlier so he has time to exercise in the morning
   (b) get to school earlier since he took the day off today
   (c) stay home and rest

III Speaking

A. Use 能不能 to ask a friend if you can do something together according to your (fictional) schedule, shown below.

早上八点: 做运动

中午十二点: 去饭馆

下午四点: 做作业

B. What daily activity do you want to do a little earlier or a little later? If you can, explain why. Use complete Chinese sentences to answer.

IV Reading

A. Read the following dialogue and mark the statements that follow true (T) or false (F).

Wenwen:	爸爸，我明天能不能请假啊？
Wenwen's dad:	你为什么要请假？
Wenwen:	因为我觉得很累，明天我想晚点儿起床。
Wenwen's dad:	你明天不能请假。你喝点儿水，今天晚上早点儿睡觉吧！而且你得经常做运动。明天早上你能不能跟我一起做运动？
Wenwen:	做运动更累啊……那我今天晚上早点儿睡觉吧。

	T	F
1. Wenwen wants to take the day off tomorrow.	○	○
2. Wenwen says she is very tired and unhappy.	○	○
3. Wenwen's dad says that she can take the day off tomorrow.	○	○
4. Wenwen's dad tells her to drink some water, go to sleep earlier tonight, and exercise often.	○	○

B. Create a logical dialogue by filling in each blank with the letter of the appropriate sentence that follows.

Huanhuan: 我今天中午不太想做饭，我想去饭馆吃饭。

Tiantian: 我也想去饭馆吃饭。 1. _____

Huanhuan: 能啊！我们去天天饭馆吧。 2. _____

Tiantian: 太好了，我最喜欢吃面条！ 3. _____

Huanhuan: 那我们早点儿去吧！十一点怎么样？

Tiantian: 4. _____

(a) 我能吃两份面条！

(b) 那个饭馆的面条挺好吃的。

(c) 好啊，我也想早点儿去。

(d) 我能跟你一起去吗？

V | Writing

A. Read each answer, then use the words and phrases below the question line to write a meaningful question.

1. Q: _____

不能 ┊ 请假？ ┊ 我明天 ┊ 能

A: 你明天不能请假。

2. Q: _____

水？ ｜ 点儿 ｜ 喝 ｜ 不要 ｜ 你 ｜ 要

A: 好啊，我想喝点儿水。谢谢！

3. Q: _____

篮球场？ ｜ 去 ｜ 早一点儿 ｜ 能不能 ｜ 你周末

A: 能啊。

B. Use the phrases in the list to complete the conversation between Isabella and Emma.

Choices: 早点儿吃饭，几点，喝点儿水，能不能 ，七点，
早点儿睡觉

妈妈，我们今天 _____ 吃饭？

我们 _____ 吃饭。

我们 _____ 早点儿吃饭？

你今天为什么想 _____ ？

因为我很累，想 _____ 。

好吧，你 _____ ，我现在去给你和马丁
做饭吧。

Expressing slight discomfort

Audio

I Pinyin and Tone

A. Listen to the recording and place a check on the line for each word that ends with the final sound -e.

1. _____   2. _____   3. _____   4. _____   5. _____   6. _____

Audio

II Listening

A. Listen as the speaker talks about how she feels, then mark the letter of the item that will make her feel better.

1. _____   2. _____   3. _____   4. _____   5. _____   6. _____

B. Listen to each question, then listen to the three possible answers. Mark the letter of the statement that best answers each question.

1. (a) (b) (c)

2. (a) (b) (c)

3. (a) (b) (c)

III Speaking

A. You are in a gym class in China and have started to feel a little bit tired, hot, and thirsty. Tell your teacher how you feel and ask for permission to rest and drink some water.

B. Imagine that your friend is asking for restaurant recommendations, and you think the restaurant you went to yesterday served delicious food. How would you tell your friend about the restaurant in Chinese?

IV Reading

A. Read Miko's journal entry and mark the statements that follow true (T) or false (F).

我今天早上请假了，没去上课，因为我觉得不太舒服。我有的时候觉得很冷，有的时候觉得很热。妈妈说我得喝点儿水，在家休息。爸爸给我做了很多好吃的菜。我喝了很多水，吃了爸爸做的菜。我现在不渴，也不饿。我还在家听了我最喜欢听的音乐。下午我觉得好点儿了。

	T	F
1. Miko took the day off from school yesterday but went back to school today.	○	○
2. Miko took the day off because she wasn't feeling well.	○	○
3. Miko's mom said she should drink some water and rest at home.	○	○
4. Miko's dad ordered food for her from a restaurant.	○	○
5. Miko didn't want to eat or drink anything, so now she's hungry and thirsty.	○	○
6. Miko listened to her favorite music.	○	○

B. Create a logical dialogue by filling in each blank with the letter of the appropriate sentence that follows.

 你好，大文！今天不冷也不热，挺舒服的。

1. _____

 你好！2. _____ 可是我现在有点儿渴，还有点儿饿。

 那我们现在去吃饭吧。3. _____

 你说的是天天饭馆吧？我也很喜欢去那儿吃饭。

4. _____

(a) 我也想去打网球，

(b) 我们去那个饺子很好吃的饭馆，怎么样？

(c) 你想去学校打网球吗？

(d) 那我们现在去吃饭，下午一点半去学校的网球场打网球吧！

V Writing

A. Use the words and phrases in the list to complete the conversation between the girl and her older brother.

Choices: 冷，热，渴，饿，舒服，休息，有点儿，的，点儿

Younger sister: 你不觉得 _____ 吗？

Older brother: 不冷啊！我觉得很 _____。你冷吗？

Younger sister:	我 _____ 冷。
Older brother:	那你喝 _____ _____ 水，怎么样？
Younger sister:	可是我不 _____……
Older brother:	那你吃点儿我做 _____ 饭吧？
Younger sister:	我也不 _____……
Older brother:	啊？你觉得不舒服吗？
Younger sister:	我有一点儿不舒服，我想去 _____。
Older brother:	好！那你去休息吧！

B. Look at the photo below. How do you think the man is feeling? What do you think he wants? Write your answers in complete Chinese sentences on the lines provided.

_____

_____

Getting sick

Audio

I Pinyin and Tone

A. Listen to the recording, then circle the characters that have the -ao final and underline the ones that have the -ou final.

1. 冒   2. 头   3. 有   4. 烧   5. 早   6. 肉

B. You will hear a list of two-character words and phrases. If both characters have the same tone, place a check on the line next to that word or phrase.

1. 发烧 ___   2. 感冒 ___   3. 休息 ___

4. 头疼 ___   5. 开始 ___   6. 重要 ___

Audio

II Listening

A. Listen to the voicemail Owen received from Miko and mark the statements that follow true (T) or false (F).

	T	F
1. Miko is sick and cannot come to class.	○	○
2. Miko learned from her teacher that Owen is sick.	○	○
3. Miko asks if she can go to Owen's house to visit him tomorrow.	○	○

B. Listen to the phone conversation between two classmates and answer the questions that follow.

1. Why did the boy call the girl?
   - (a) He wants to know why she didn't go to school today.
   - (b) He wants to go to school with her tomorrow.
   - (c) He needs help with homework.

2. How does the girl say she is feeling?
   - (a) She has a bit of a cold but no fever or headache.
   - (b) She has a bit of a headache, and she's in a bad mood.
   - (c) She has a cold, a fever, and a headache.

3. What does the boy suggest that the girl do?
   - (a) He tells her to drink cold water and go to bed early when she takes a day off.
   - (b) He tells her to drink hot water and go to sleep earlier when she has a cold.
   - (c) He tells her to study more because today's classes were difficult.

III Speaking

A. All of the people in the photos below are feeling sick. Use complete Chinese sentences to describe their symptoms and state what they might want to do to feel better.

IV Reading

A. Read what Sanjay and Leo have messaged each other and mark the statements that follow true (T) or false (F).

 我知道你昨天生病了。你今天觉得怎么样？

 我感冒了，不太舒服，头有点儿疼，可是不发烧。我喝了很多热水，因为我妈妈说感冒的时候得喝热水。

 是啊，那你现在得在家休息。今天的历史课挺难的。作业也挺多的。

 那你能不能教我啊？

 可以啊！那我现在给你打电话吧？

 太好了，谢谢！

	T	F
1. Leo asks if Sanjay is coming to school today.	○	○
2. Sanjay has a bad headache and a fever.	○	○
3. Sanjay has been drinking a lot of hot water because he feels thirsty.	○	○
4. Leo will call Sanjay to teach him what he learned in history class today.	○	○

B. Read the notes on the medical record (病历单 bìnglì dān) below and mark the statements that follow true (T) or false (F).

病 历 单
星期一：不舒服，想睡觉。
不发烧，有点儿头疼。
星期二：开始发烧。头很
疼，不想吃饭。
星期三：不发烧。头不疼。
可以吃一点儿饭。

T F

1. The patient was running a fever from Monday to Wednesday. ○ ○

2. The patient had a severe headache on Tuesday. ○ ○

3. The patient still had a good appetite on Tuesday. ○ ○

C. Read the dialogue and mark the statements that follow true (T) or false (F).

Boy: 你最喜欢什么时候听音乐？

Girl: 我最喜欢做作业的时候听音乐，因为听音乐的时候我不觉得紧张。

Boy: 我跟你不一样。我做作业的时候不喜欢听音乐。我喜欢做运动的时候听音乐。我觉得听音乐的时候做运动更有意思！我感冒的时候也喜欢听音乐。听音乐的时候，我觉得能舒服一点儿。

T F

1. The girl says she doesn't feel anxious when she listens to music, so she likes listening to music when she does homework. ○ ○

2. The boy thinks exercise is more enjoyable when he listens to music. ○ ○

3. The boy also likes to listen to music when he has a cold. ○ ○

A. Rearrange the Chinese words and phrases to translate the English sentences.

1. I have a bit of a headache today.

_____

头疼。 ┊ 有一点儿 ┊ 我今天

2. When Daming has a cold, he likes to drink hot water.

_____

喜欢 ┊ 热 ┊ 喝 ┊ 大明感冒 ┊ 的时候 ┊ 水。

3. Martin got a fever, so he asked for a sick day today.

_____

马丁 ┊ 请假了。 ┊ 他今天 ┊ 发烧了， ┊ 所以

B. The girl on the right is talking to her sister, who is sick. Use your imagination and write a list of some suggestions she might be giving her sister.

_____

_____

_____

Put the Pieces Together!

I Chapter Vocabulary Chart

Fill in the pinyin for and the definition of each word that you learned in this chapter. Use the extra spaces at the end of the chart to add any additional words you learned.

No.	Word	Pinyin	Definition
1	能		
2	请假		
3	晚		
4	（一）点儿		
5	喝		
6	水		
7	早		
8	冷		
9	热		
10	舒服		
11	渴		

No.	Word	Pinyin	Definition
12	休息		
13	饿		
14	生病		
15	感冒		
16	头		
17	疼		
18	发烧		
19	来		

II Reading

A. Read Ellen's journal entry and answer the questions that follow.

今天挺冷的，我很晚才起床。我感冒了，觉得不太舒服。我不发烧，可是有点儿头疼。我还觉得有点儿渴，所以我喝了点儿热水。妈妈做的饭很好吃，可是我今天不太想吃饭，因为我不觉得饿。我们生病的时候不能去学校，所以我今天请假了。老师早上给我打电话了，他说："你在家休息吧。"我说："好，谢谢老师！那我明天能不能也请假？"

1. What does Ellen say about her sleep schedule?
   (a) She didn't go to sleep until very late last night.
   (b) She went to bed early last night and woke up early this morning.
   (c) She woke up late this morning.

2. What are Ellen's symptoms?
   (a) She has a fever and a bad headache.
   (b) She has a fever and a bit of a headache.
   (c) She has a bit of a headache, but no fever.

3. Why has Ellen not been eating much?
   (a) She's been so busy, she hasn't had time to eat.
   (b) The food her mom makes isn't very tasty.
   (c) She's not very hungry, even though her mom makes tasty food.

4. What did Ellen's teacher say when she took the day off?
   (a) He said that she must come to school since she is not very sick.
   (b) He said that she should stay home and rest.
   (c) He said that he is sick, too, so she doesn't need to come to school.

III Writing

A. Imagine that you are sick this evening. Write an email to your Chinese teacher to describe your symptoms and to let your teacher know that you need to take a day off and rest tomorrow.

_____

_____

Looking for Support

Can-Do Goals

In this chapter, you are learning to:

- Understand ways Chinese students might look for academic support

- Discuss doing something again

- Understand when someone describes a sequence of events

- Talk about completing a task

- Advise someone to do more or less of something

- Express things that will happen or that could happen

Again?

Audio

I Pinyin and Tone

A. Listen to the recording and place a check on the line provided for each word that has the z- initial sound.

1. _____ 2. _____ 3. _____ 4. _____ 5. _____ 6. _____

B. Listen to the recording and circle the fourth-tone characters. Note: In some of the words below, both of the characters are fourth tone!

1. 然后 2. 最后 3. 问题 4. 感冒 5. 饭馆 6. 不用

Audio

II Listening

A. Listen as the speaker talks about her plans for this Saturday. In the numbered spaces, write the letter of each place she will go to show the sequence of her activities for that day.

1. _____ 2. _____ 3. _____ 4. _____

a

b

c

d

B. Listen to the dialogue and mark the following statements true (T) or false (F).

	T	F
1. When the speaker couldn't do his math homework, he asked only his classmates for help.	○	○
2. The speaker has already asked five questions about today's math homework.	○	○
3. After asking questions, the speaker still feels that he can't do the homework.	○	○
4. The speaker is going to ask his older sister a few questions, too.	○	○

III Speaking

A. Use 先, 再, 然后, and 最后 to describe what 明明 wants to do today, as indicated by the images below.

IV Reading

A. Read the passage below and draw four pictures to show what happens in the story. Make sure to draw the pictures in the correct order of events!

今天下午我先跟朋友看了一个电影，然后我跟爸爸在家做了面条，最后我和弟弟去打篮球了。晚上，妈妈问了我一个问题，"你还没开始做作业吗？"我说："我现在去做作业，妈妈！"

1.	2.
3.	**4.**

B. Read the dialogue below and mark the statements that follow true (T) or false (F).

我今天又去打网球了。打网球太有意思了！

我也很喜欢打网球！你明天还想再去打网球吗？

想！可是我明天很忙。我得先做历史作业，然后去给我朋友买生日礼物……

那你先做历史作业，然后我们去打网球，最后我跟你一起去给你朋友买生日礼物，怎么样？

好主意！

	T	F
1. Ellen played tennis for the first time today.	○	○
2. Sanjay does not like to play tennis.	○	○
3. Ellen needs to do science homework and buy a birthday gift for her friend tomorrow.	○	○
4. Sanjay suggests that Ellen first do her homework, then play tennis with him, and finally go with him to buy a birthday gift for her friend.	○	○
5. Ellen does not agree with Sanjay's plan.	○	○

V Writing

A. Rearrange the Chinese words and phrases to translate the English sentences.

1. Can I eat first and then exercise?

再 ┊ 先 ┊ 我可以 ┊ 吃饭， ┊ 去做运动吗？

2. Haven't you started doing your homework yet?

做作业 ┊ 没 ┊ 你 ┊ 开始 ┊ 吗？ ┊ 还

3. I want to go to the neighborhood pet shop first and then go to my teacher's house to learn erhu.

_____

| 再去 | 学二胡。 | 我要 | 小区的 | 先去 | 宠物店， |
| 老师家 |

4. I ordered the red-cooked pork first, then the dumplings, and finally the noodles.

_____

| 点了一份面条。 | 最后 | 然后 | 点了一份饺子， |
| 点了一份红烧肉， | 我 | 先 |

B. Below is Owen's to do list for this Sunday. Use sequencing words such as 先, 再, 然后, and 最后 to describe what he will do.

to do list:

☐ 给弟弟买生日礼物 _____

☐ 吹笛子 _____

☐ 去饭馆吃红烧肉 _____

☐ 做历史作业 _____

_____

_____

_____

Study plans

Audio

I Pinyin and Tone

A. Listen to the recording. Circle the words that have the -ü final (the sound that you hear in words like 去). Underline the words that have the -u final (the sound that you hear in words like 书).

1. 不   2. 区   3. 去   4. 五   5. 预   6. 复

B. Listen to the recording and put a check next to the number of each word that has the -ue final sound.

1. _____   2. _____   3. _____   4. _____   5. _____

Audio

II Listening

A. Listen to the dialogue and mark the following statements true (T) or false (F).

		T	F
1.	The boy asks the girl how she feels this month.	○	○
2.	The girl's study plan is to preview her lessons before class and review them after class.	○	○
3.	The boy plans to read more Chinese books and watch more TV.	○	○

B. Listen to the dialogue and mark the following statements true (T) or false (F).

		T	F
1.	The speaker sometimes previews her lessons first.	○	○
2.	Today, the speaker's Chinese teacher told her that she must first complete her homework and then preview what they will be learning tomorrow.	○	○
3.	The speaker does not like the plan.	○	○

III Speaking

A. Talk about your plans for this week. What do you plan to do more and what do you plan to do less?

IV Reading

A. Read Tiantian's study plan and mark the statements that follow true (T) or false (F).

学习计划	
星期一	预习明天的中文课，做完数学作业
星期二	复习数学，预习明天的科学课
星期三	做完中文作业，预习明天的历史课
星期四	复习中文，做完科学作业
星期五	做完历史作业，复习科学课和历史课

	T	F
1. Tiantian plans to review Chinese and finish his math homework on Monday.	○	○
2. Tiantian plans to review math and preview science on Tuesday.	○	○
3. Tiantian plans to do Chinese homework and review history on Wednesday.	○	○
4. Tiantian plans to review science and history on both Thursday and Friday.	○	○

B. Read the sentences below and number them in the correct order to create a logical conversation. The first sentence has been numbered for you.

_1_ Mingming: 我朋友告诉了我一个很有意思的电影。我们星期六一起去看吧。

___ Mingming: 那好吧。我们星期六见！

___ Wenwen: 我可以去看电影，可是我不想去饭馆吃饭。我计划多在家吃饭，少去饭馆。

___ Wenwen: 我挺想去的。可是我得先预习完中文、复习完数学，然后和你去看电影。

___ Mingming: 好，那你星期六先预习中文和复习数学吧。看完电影，你想去饭馆吃饭吗？

A. Rearrange the Chinese words and phrases to make logical sentences.

1. _____

再上课。┊ 先预习，┊ 你得

2. _____

告诉 ┊ 我 ┊ 昨天老师 ┊ 学习计划。┊ 一个

3. _____

多看 ┊ 乒乓球。┊ 少 ┊ 打 ┊ 我计划 ┊ 书，

4. _____

然后复习。┊ 做完作业，┊ 先 ┊ 我一定要

B. Write a study plan for any class you choose. Try to describe which days of the week you go to class, when and where you plan to complete your homework, and when you plan to preview and/or review what you have learned.

_____

_____

_____

_____

_____

Expressing what will happen

I   Pinyin and Tone

Audio

A. First, listen to the recording of the words 七 and 吃. In the word 七, the final -i has a long "ee" sound while in the word 吃 it has a shorter sound. Then, look at the list of words below and listen to the recording. If the character in the grey box has the same vowel sound as 七, circle it. If the character in the grey box is read with the same vowel sound as 吃, underline it.

Long sound: 七

Short sound: 吃

1. 计划   2. 复习   3. 迟到   4. 收拾   5. 东西   6. 时候

II   Listening

Audio

A. You will hear four brief statements. Write the letter of the image that matches each statement you hear.

1. ____   2. ____   3. ____   4. ____

B. Listen to each "if" phrase, and then listen to the three possible choices to complete the sentence. Mark the letter of the statement that best completes each sentence.

1. (a) (b) (c)

2. (a) (b) (c)

3. (a) (b) (c)

III Speaking

A. Under what circumstances might you be late for school? Use 如果 ... 我会 ... to answer this question.

B. Imagine you are shopping for clothes with a friend, and you don't like the piece of clothing your friend is considering. What could you say? (Hint: Use 别.)

IV Reading

A. Read Leo and Martin's messages to each other and mark the statements that follow true (T) or false (F).

 马丁，你好！我今天早上觉得很累，所以七点四十才起床。我现在还在家收拾东西，我觉得我今天会迟到……如果上科学课的时候，我还没来，你能帮我告诉老师吗？

 好！如果上科学课的时候，你还没来，我会告诉老师你会晚点儿来。今天我们可以一起做科学作业。如果你有问题，你可以问我。

 太好了！谢谢！

	T	F
1. Leo is running late because it took him too long to pack his backpack this morning.	○	○
2. Leo asks Martin to tell the teacher that Leo is sick.	○	○
3. Leo thinks that he might be late to science class.	○	○
4. Leo appreciates Martin's suggestion that they do their science homework together today.	○	○

B. Read the dialogue and mark the statements that follow true (T) or false (F).

我们现在去打乒乓球吧！

可是我还没收拾完明天上课的东西！我想先收拾东西，再去打乒乓球。

你别收拾了。你可以明天早上收拾东西啊！

如果我明天早上才收拾东西，我一定会迟到。我不想迟到……

好吧，你要我帮你收拾东西吗？

不用了，谢谢！

	T	F
1. Isabella wants to finish her homework before playing ping-pong with Ellen.	○	○
2. Ellen suggests that Isabella pack up her things tomorrow morning.	○	○
3. Isabella thinks Ellen's suggestion is a good idea.	○	○
4. Ellen offers to help Isabella with her homework.	○	○

V Writing

A. Use the words in the list to complete the sentences. Use each word only once.

Choices: 如果，帮，收拾，会，迟到

1. ＿＿＿＿＿＿ 我明天不能来学校，你能 ＿＿＿＿＿＿ 我请假吗？

2. 他每天睡觉都很晚，所以经常 ＿＿＿＿＿＿。

3. 你 ＿＿＿＿＿＿ 每天先 ＿＿＿＿＿＿ 东西，再睡觉吗？

B. Write captions to describe the images below. If there is a change in situation, remember to use 了 !

1. _____

2. _____

3. _____

4. _____

Put the Pieces Together!

I Chapter Vocabulary Chart

Fill in the pinyin for and the definition of each word that you learned in this chapter. Use the extra spaces at the end of the chart to add any additional words you learned.

No.	Word	Pinyin	Definition
1	又		
2	问题		
3	还		
4	再		
5	先		
6	然后		
7	最后		
8	告诉		
9	学习		
10	计划		
11	完		

No.	Word	Pinyin	Definition
12	预习		
13	复习		
14	少		
15	别		
16	如果		
17	收拾		
18	东西		
19	会		
20	迟到		
21	帮		

II Reading

A. Read Sanjay's journal entry below and answer the questions that follow.

我想做一个中文学习计划，所以我今天去问白老师了。他说最好的计划是先预习，再上课，然后做完每天的作业。我不会做作业的时候要告诉他，因为他可以帮我复习。我现在能说不少中文了。所以白老师还说，我可以和中国朋友一起学习，多说中文，少说英文。然后，不迟到也很重要。我可以晚上收拾完上课的东西。他说如果我还有问题，我可以再去问他。

1. What did Sanjay ask Mr. Bai (his teacher) today?
   (a) He asked what Mr. Bai's favorite Chinese restaurant is.
   (b) He asked what today's homework assignment is.
   (c) He asked how to make a study plan for Chinese class.

2. Which of the following is a suggestion that Mr. Bai gave to Sanjay?
   (a) Sanjay should preview his lessons more and review his lessons less.
   (b) Sanjay should ask his Chinese friends for help before doing his homework.
   (c) Sanjay should speak more Chinese and less English with his Chinese friends.

3. What did Mr. Bai say that he can do for Sanjay?
   (a) If Sanjay can't do his homework, Mr. Bai can help Sanjay review.
   (b) He can tell Sanjay the answers to the homework questions.
   (c) He can excuse Sanjay from being late to class.

4. What extra suggestion did Mr. Bai include in the study plan he recommended to Sanjay?
   (a) Sanjay should pack his class materials up the night before class instead of in the morning.
   (b) Sanjay should watch less TV every day.
   (c) Sanjay should make a lot of new Chinese friends.

III Writing

A. What kind of study plan do you think best prepares a student for success? Use at least three of the four suggestions here to write about habits that you think make a student successful.

- Use 先 … 再 … 然后 … 最后 … to say the best order in which to do things
- Use 如果 to say what a student should do if he/she has questions
- Use 别 to say what a successful student shouldn't do
- Use 又 or 再 to say what successful students may have to do more than once

_____

_____

_____

_____

Making Progress

Can-Do Goals

In this chapter, you are learning to:

- Explore fun activities to support Chinese learning outside the classroom

- Describe your impression of different activities

- Say that you or others were mistaken in their thinking

- Discuss what you have done before

- Understand when someone emphasizes what something is or who someone is

- Describe how a situation changes over time

Learning Chinese

Audio

I Pinyin and Tone

A. Many of the new words in this section use the third tone. Listen to the recording and circle each character that is read in the third tone.

1. 以前　　2. 以为　　3. 起来　　4. 懂　　5. 语法

Audio

II Listening

A. Listen to the dialogue and mark the following statements true (T) or false (F).

		T	F
1.	The boy asks the girl what today's homework is.	○	○
2.	The girl thought today's homework looked easy but has found that it is actually difficult.	○	○
3.	The girl finished the homework early and is doing something else now.	○	○

B. Listen to each question, then listen to the three possible answers. Mark the letter of the statement that best answers each question.

1. ⓐ ⓑ ⓒ

2. ⓐ ⓑ ⓒ

3. ⓐ ⓑ ⓒ

III Speaking

A. Use 起来 to talk about something that seems different than it really is. For instance, is there a dish that you think looks bad but tastes good? Or a movie you thought looked interesting but turned out to be boring?

B. Talk about your impression of one of your classes. Is your impression now different than it was in the past? Try to use words such as 以前, 以为, 但是, 起来, and 容易 in your answer.

Ⅳ Reading

A. Read the sentences below, then write the letter of the image that best matches each sentence on the line provided.

1. 我已经开始学习中文语法了。你看，这个语法很好懂。___

2. 这个主意听起来不错。___

3. 她觉得这门课看起来挺难的。___

4. 她觉得数学学起来很容易。___

B. Read the passage below about Martin's thoughts on learning Chinese. Then mark the statements that follow true (T) or false (F).

以前我以为学中文不重要，但是现在我觉得学中文很重要。中文和英文的语法很不一样，但是中文的语法不难懂。而且我很喜欢学习不一样的东西，所以我觉得中文学起来很有意思。我还觉得中文很好听！我计划看更多的中文书，多说中文。

	T	F
1. Martin has always thought that studying Chinese is important.	○	○
2. Martin thinks that Chinese grammar is difficult to understand.	○	○
3. Martin likes studying Chinese because he thinks that Chinese grammar is quite similar to English grammar.	○	○

V Writing

A. In the following passage, a student describes his experience learning English. Use the words in the list to complete the sentences. Use each word only once.

Choices: 以前，容易，语法，起来，但是，懂，以为

_____，我不喜欢看英文语法书。_____
现在，我很喜欢学英文语法！英文的语法跟中文
的 _____ 很不一样，所以以前我 _____
英文学起来不太 _____。我生日的时候，我
姐姐送了我一本很好 _____ 的语法书。那
本书我已经看完了，所以现在我觉得英文语法学
_____ 很有意思！

B. Read each question, then use the words below the Answer line to write a meaningful answer.

1.**Q:** 这是什么书？

  A: _____

  一本 ┊ 语法 ┊ 中文 ┊ 这 ┊ 是 ┊ 书。

2.**Q:** 你觉得这本书好懂吗？

  A: _____

  好懂！ ┊ 我 ┊ 本 ┊ 觉得 ┊ 这 ┊ 很 ┊ 书

3.**Q:** 你要看这本书吗？

  A: _____

  不太 ┊ 我 ┊ 看 ┊ 种 ┊ 想 ┊ 这 ┊ 书……

Discussing past experiences

I Pinyin and Tone

Audio

A. You will hear a recording of the words 就 (jiù) and 周 (zhōu) said several times. Keep a tally as you listen to the recording and write the final count for each word on the lines provided.

Number of times I heard 就 : _____

Number of times I heard 周 : _____

II Listening

Audio

A. Listen to the dialogue and mark the following statements true (T) or false (F).

	T	F
1. The correct answer to the question is A.	○	○
2. The boy got the question wrong, but his friend told him the correct answer.	○	○
3. The girl knows the correct answer.	○	○
4. At the end of the conversation, the girl says goodbye to the boy.	○	○

B. Listen to the dialogue and mark the following statements true (T) or false (F).

	T	F
1. The boy asks the girl if she is listening to Chinese music.	○	○
2. The girl has heard Chinese music before.	○	○
3. The boy knows how to play the erhu and can teach the girl.	○	○
4. The girl does not want to learn how to play the erhu.	○	○

III Speaking

A. Imagine that you and a friend are having a conversation about sports. Your friend says he often plays soccer, but he has never played ping-pong because his school doesn't have a ping-pong table. Tell your friend which sports you have played before and mention one sport you haven't played yet (if there is one) and why.

B. Ellen, Miko, and Sanjay have recently taken a test. The chart below shows the correct answers for two questions on the test as well as the answers given by Ellen, Miko, and Sanjay for those two questions. In Chinese, state what the correct answer is for each question and whether each student answered correctly or incorrectly. Try using 就 for emphasis!

答案	Ellen	Miko	Sanjay
1	A	B	B	A
2	B	B	B	A

IV Reading

A. Read the dialogue between Owen and his online tutor, Daming, then mark the statements that follow true (T) or false (F).

我以前做过这个题，我知道这个题的答案。
答案就是 A。我的答案没有错，但是科学老师
为什么说我的答案错了？

你再看，这个题跟你做过的题一样吗？

啊，我知道了！这两个题不一样。谢谢！

不客气。

	T	F
1. Owen thinks he has done this problem before and is confident the answer is A.	○	○
2. Owen is asking Daming about a math problem.	○	○
3. Daming agrees that the answer is A.	○	○
4. Daming tells Owen to look at the problem again.	○	○
5. Daming says 不客气 because he thinks Owen is a very impolite student.	○	○

B. Read the dialogue and mark the statements that follow true (T) or false (F).

你今天为什么看起来不太高兴？

我昨天请假了，没去上课，所以我不会做今天的数学作业。

我已经做完数学作业了。我可以帮你。

那太好了！这个题的答案是 A 吗？那个题的答案是 B 吗？

这个题的答案就是 A！可是，那个题的答案错了。

那个题太难了，我不太懂。

我做过那个题。我教你吧！

           T   **F**

1. Leo is in a good mood because he thinks today's homework is easy. ○ ○

2. Maya knows how to do today's homework. ○ ○

3. Leo's answers for the two homework questions are both wrong. ○ ○

C. Read the sentences below and number them in the correct order to create a logical conversation. The first sentence has been done for you.

_1_	Student:	你好！你是这个音乐学校的老师吗？
___	Student:	我叫林小明。谢谢老师！
___	Teacher:	对，我就是这个学校的老师！
___	Teacher:	我就是教古筝的老师。我可以教你。你叫什么名字？
___	Student:	老师好！我能在这儿选古筝课吗？我没学过古筝，但是我觉得古筝太好听了，我很想学。

V | Writing

A. Rearrange the Chinese words and phrases to translate the English sentences.

1. The teacher said my answer was wrong.

答案 ｜ 我 ｜ 错 ｜ 的 ｜ 了。 ｜ 老师 ｜ 说

2. They have never been to Beijing.

北京。 ｜ 过 ｜ 没 ｜ 他们 ｜ 去

3. You are too polite!

客气 ｜ 了! ｜ 你们 ｜ 太

4. This is exactly the movie I want to see.

这 ｜ 电影。 ｜ 就是 ｜ 我 ｜ 看 ｜ 想 ｜ 的

B. The table below lists some things Huanhuan and Tiantian have and have not done before. Use complete Chinese sentences to write about what they have and haven't done.

	做过	没有做过
欢欢	吃中国菜，去中国朋友家	做中国菜
天天	吃中国菜	去中国朋友家

Better and better

I | Pinyin and Tone

Audio

A. Complete the pinyin with the initial sounds x, c, or sh.

1. liàn____í
2. ____ēng____í
3. ____iě
4. yì____iē
5. bú____uò

B. Look at the following pairs of words, which sound identical except for the tone. You will hear one word from each pair; circle the word you hear.

1. xiě 写   xiē 些

2. tí 题   tī 踢

3. jiù 就   jiǔ 九

4. dǒng 懂   dòng 动

5. dǎ 打   dá 答

6. guò 过   guó 国

II | Listening

Audio

A. Listen to the passage and mark the following statements true (T) or false (F).

	T	F
1. The speaker finds she likes writing Chinese characters more and more.	○	○
2. The speaker only practices writing Chinese characters on the weekend.	○	○
3. The speaker wants to practice writing Chinese characters more often.	○	○
4. The speaker thinks that if she practices every day, she'll be able to write more and more Chinese characters.	○	○

B. Listen to the dialogue and mark the following statements true (T) or false (F).

	T	F
1. The teacher asks if the student has previewed the new words.	○	○
2. The student says he practiced using the new grammar.	○	○
3. The teacher says the student's pronunciation will get better and better if he practices every day.	○	○

III Speaking

A. There are many things that are a part of learning Chinese, including talking in Chinese, watching Chinese movies, reading Chinese books, studying new vocabulary, practicing pronunciation, and writing Chinese characters. Use Chinese to talk about which you think are most important to do every day, and why.

IV Reading

A. Read the dialogue below and mark the statements that follow true (T) or false (F).

你今天为什么看起来有点儿累？

我的中文作业越来越多了！我得练习发音，预习生词，还得写很多汉字。昨天我十一点才睡觉！

你昨天才开始做作业吗？这些作业是一个星期的作业。如果你每天都做点儿作业，你一定能早一点儿做完。

这个主意挺好的。我要做一个更好的学习计划，每天都做些作业！

	T	F
1. Owen's Chinese homework includes practicing pronunciation, previewing new words, and writing lots of Chinese characters.	○	○
2. Ellen tells Owen to watch less TV if he wants to finish his homework earlier.	○	○
3. Ellen seems to have a better study plan than Owen.	○	○
4. Owen decides to do some of his Chinese homework every day.	○	○

B. A Chinese language teacher has written the plan for the day's class on the whiteboard. What will students be doing? (Answer in English.)

一. 预习第八课
二. 复习昨天的作业
三. 做练习
四. 听第八课的录音
五. 看书

_____

_____

V Writing

A. Complete the translation of each sentence.

1. I should practice the new words we learned today more.

我得多 _____ 今天学的生词。

2. Which Chinese characters can you write?

你会写哪些 _____ ？

3. I learned many new words today.

我今天学了很多 _____ 。

4. My teacher says my pronunciation has gotten better and better.

老师说，我的 _____ 越来越好 _____ 。

5. I can write more and more Chinese characters.

我会 _____ 的汉字 _____ 多了。

B. What does the girl in the illustrations below think are important to do often when learning Chinese? Based on what she's shown doing, use your imagination to mention the activities she thinks are important, using as many newly-learned words as you can.

_____

_____

_____

_____

_____

Put the Pieces Together!

I | Chapter Vocabulary Chart

Fill in the pinyin for and the definition of each word that you learned in this chapter. Use the extra spaces at the end of the chart to add any additional words you learned.

No.	Word	Pinyin	Definition
1	以前		
2	以为		
3	但是		
4	起来		
5	容易		
6	语法		
7	懂		
8	过		
9	题		
10	答案		
11	就		

No.	Word	Pinyin	Definition
12	错		
13	客气		
14	些		
15	生词		
16	练习		
17	写		
18	汉字		
19	越来越		
20	发音		

A. Read the dialogue and mark the statements that follow true (T) or false (F).

明明：　　老师，这个题的答案是 A 吗？

林老师：对，答案就是 A！

明明：　　这个题的语法有点儿难，所以我以为我的答案错了。

林老师：你的答案对了。我以前告诉过你们，中文的语法很简单。如果你们多看中国电影、多听中国音乐，一定会觉得中文语法越来越好学。

明明：　　对，谢谢老师！我现在觉得中文学起来越来越有意思了。我每天都会练习写些汉字，还会跟我朋友一起说中文。林老师，你觉得我的发音现在怎么样？

林老师：你的发音也越来越好了！

明明：　　太好了，谢谢老师！

林老师：不客气！

	T	F
1. Ms. Lin tells Mingming that his answer is wrong.	○	○
2. Mingming does not quite understand the grammar in the question at first.	○	○
3. Ms. Lin told her students not to watch Chinese movies, since the Chinese spoken in them is too difficult.	○	○
4. Minging thinks that learning Chinese is getting more and more interesting.	○	○
5. Mingming reviews new vocabulary and practices writing Chinese characters every day.	○	○
6. Mingming asks Ms. Lin how to improve his Chinese pronunciation.	○	○

III Writing

A. Isabella has written a "Then and Now" chart for the progress she has made in learning Chinese. Write a summary of her progress.

以前	现在
以为中文不太好学	觉得中文越来越好学了
不喜欢学生词	每天学些生词
不太看中文书，觉得中文的语法有点儿难	经常看中文书，觉得中文的语法很好懂
不太会做题，所以很多题的答案错了	每个题都会做，作业的答案都对了

_____

_____

_____

_____

_____

School and Activities

Can-Do Goals

In this chapter, you are learning to:

- Name some of the types of student clubs available in Chinese schools

- Discuss joining student clubs

- Understand when others express how well they do something

- Make contrasting statements

- Talk about something you are hoping for

Doing things well

Audio

I Pinyin and Tone

A. The characters 为, 觉, and 得 are 多音字, or characters with more than one pronunciation. Listen to the recording. You will hear unfamiliar words made up of characters you know and one of the three 多音字 mentioned above. Check either (a) or (b) to indicate the correct pronunciation of the circled character. The first one has been done for you.

1. 为人 ✓ (a) wéi (as in 以为) ____ (b) wèi (as in 因为)
2. 为了 ____ (a) wéi (as in 以为) ____ (b) wèi (as in 因为)
3. 午觉 ____ (a) jué (as in 觉得) ____ (b) jiào (as in 睡觉)
4. 感觉 ____ (a) jué (as in 觉得) ____ (b) jiào (as in 睡觉)
5. 得要 ____ (a) děi (as in 得) ____ (b) de (as in 觉得)
6. 懂得 ____ (a) děi (as in 得) ____ (b) de (as in 觉得)

Audio

II Listening

A. You will hear three statements. Write the letter of the image that shows the appropriate gesture to go along with each statement.

1. ____   2. ____   3. ____

a   b   c

B. Listen to each question, then listen to the three possible answers. Mark the letter of the statement that best answers each question.

1. (a) (b) (c)

2. (a) (b) (c)

3. (a) (b) (c)

III Speaking

A. Your Chinese friend is telling you about the club he belongs to at his school. How would you ask him if he has gotten to know any new friends at the club? What other questions would you ask him to learn more about the club?

B. Are there any activities you feel you do fairly well or not so well? Use 得 to talk about one thing you're good at and another thing you're not good at.

IV Reading

A. Read the dialogue and mark the statements that follow true (T) or false (F).

你最近怎么样?

挺好的! 我最近加入了乒乓球俱乐部。我在那儿认识了很多新朋友。我们经常一起打乒乓球。现在我乒乓球打得越来越好了。

什么俱乐部? 乒乓球俱乐部? 这个俱乐部听起来很有意思。我能和你一起去吗?

好啊! 明天你和我一起去吧!

	T	F
1. Leo asks Maya how she's been recently.	○	○
2. Maya recently joined the ping-pong club and made many new friends there.	○	○
3. Maya likes playing ping-pong but feels like she isn't good at it and hasn't been improving.	○	○
4. Leo thinks the ping-pong club sounds really interesting, but he doesn't have time to join.	○	○

B. Read the announcement on the blackboard and answer the questions that follow.

1. What is this announcement promoting?
   (a) a book club
   (b) a Chinese language club
   (c) a movie club

2. Based on the announcement, which of the following would you do as part of the club's activities?
   (a) make new friends and watch interesting movies
   (b) make new friends and read Chinese books
   (c) practice speaking Chinese and writing Chinese characters

3. Based on the announcement, when will the club meeting be held?
   (a) this Thursday at 4:30 p.m.
   (b) next Thursday at 4:30 p.m.
   (c) this Wednesday at 3:30 p.m.

4. In the word 教室 (jiàoshì), the character 室 (shì) means "room." Can you guess where the first meeting of the new club will be held?
   (a) Ms. Li's living room
   (b) Ms. Li's family restaurant
   (c) Ms. Li's classroom

V Writing

A. Rearrange the Chinese words and phrases to create logical sentences.

1. _____

做得 ｜ 我 ｜ 很好。 ｜ 红烧肉 ｜ 做

2. _____

些 ｜ 认识了 ｜ 新朋友。 ｜ 学中文的 ｜ 最近我

3. _____

中国电影 ｜ 她最想 ｜ 俱乐部。 ｜ 加入

4. _____

写得 ｜ 他 ｜ 挺好的。 ｜ 写汉字

B. The people in the pictures are all very good at what they do. Complete each description.

1. 他打篮球打 _____。

2. 他弹吉他 _____ 很好听。

3. 她古筝 _____ 很好。

4. 她 _____ 菜 _____ 很好。

Enjoyable activities

Audio

I Pinyin and Tone

A. Listen to the recording and complete the pinyin for the words you hear using the final sound -ia, -ian, or -iao. Then, listen to the recording a second time and try to mark the tone of each word.

1. m_____   2. t_____   3. j_____   4. l_____   5. l_____   6. x_____

Audio

II Listening

A. You will hear four descriptions. Write the letter of the image that matches each description you hear.

1. _____   2. _____   3. _____   4. _____

B. Listen to the dialogue and mark the following statements true (T) or false (F).

	T	F
1. The girl thinks the boy's dancing is very cool.	◯	◯
2. The girl probably can't dance at all herself.	◯	◯
3. The boy wants to dance and have fun with the others at the Dance Club.	◯	◯
4. The boy and the girl agree to meet tomorrow afternoon.	◯	◯

III Speaking

A. Imagine that your friend has been complaining to you about how bored he or she is every day after school. Use 应该 to tell your friend what you think he or she should do (learn an instrument, play sports, join a club, etc.) and why.

B. Here is a song Maya learned in Chinese Club to celebrate the new year. Read the lyrics out loud. If you can read music and like singing, try to sing the song!

Note: The word 年 (nián) means "year," and the word 大家 (dàjiā) means "everyone."

新年好

新 年 好 啊，新 年 好 啊，我 祝 大 家 新 年 好。

我 们 唱 歌，我 们 跳 舞，我 祝 大 家 新 年 好。

IV Reading

A. Read the dialogue below and mark the statements that follow true (T) or false (F).

 这儿是中文俱乐部吗？

 对！你想加入我们俱乐部吗？

 想！我很喜欢学中文，我还很喜欢唱中文歌。

 那你应该加入我们！我们每个星期都会一起学中文歌。我们唱的歌都很酷。我们还会一起跳中国舞，聊天儿。你可以和很多新朋友一起玩儿！

	T	F
1. Ellen has gone to the wrong club.	○	○
2. Ellen likes singing Chinese songs.	○	○
3. Miko says that they learn a new Chinese songs every Monday at the club.	○	○
4. Miko says that they also dance and chat at Chinese Club.	○	○

B. Read the fable below and mark the statements that follow true (T) or false (F).

		T	F
1.	At the beginning of the story, the fox asks the crow to play with her.	○	○
2.	The fox says she can sing better than the crow, so the crow sings to prove her wrong.	○	○
3.	At the end of the story, the fox has stolen the crow's food.	○	○

V | Writing

A. Rearrange the Chinese words to translate the English sentences.

1. Dance Club looks really cool!

_____

啊！ ┊ 跳舞 ┊ 起来 ┊ 看 ┊ 很 ┊ 酷 ┊ 俱乐部

2. I like to dance, but I'm not very good at it.

_____

跳舞， ┊ 我 ┊ 我 ┊ 喜欢 ┊ 得 ┊ 跳 ┊ 不太好。 ┊ 可是

3. Then you should join our club and practice with us!

_____

一起 ┊ 那 ┊ 应该 ┊ 我们俱乐部， ┊ 我们 ┊ 加入 ┊
你 ┊ 跟 ┊ 练习！

B. Based on the people's interests shown below, make recommendations on which club each person should join.

_____

_____

_____

Contrasting statements

Audio

I Pinyin and Tone

A. When typing Chinese characters on a computer or smartphone, you need to type the correct pinyin for each character. Look at the characters and listen to the recording, then choose the correct pinyin you would have to enter to type the characters.

1. 放假   (a) fanjia   (b) fangjian   (c) fangjia
2. 希望   (a) xiwang   (b) xihuan   (c) shiwang
3. 学期   (a) xuechi   (b) shuiqi   (c) xueqi
4. 成绩   (a) chengji   (b) chenji   (c) chenjin

Audio

II Listening

A. Listen to each question, then listen to the three possible answers. Mark the letter of the statement that best answers each question.

1. (a) (b) (c)
2. (a) (b) (c)
3. (a) (b) (c)
4. (a) (b) (c)

B. Listen to the passage and mark the following statements true (T) or false (F).

	T	F
1. The speaker is not very busy this semester, so she does not feel tired.	○	○
2. The speaker will often do review work, but not preview work.	○	○
3. The speaker hopes to get good grades this semester.	○	○

III Speaking

A. Your friend has invited you to a restaurant. You really want to go, but you can't. Use 虽然 ... 但是 ... to explain the situation to your friend. Make sure to tell your friend why you can't go.

B. Imagine that you have just been introduced to an exchange student from China. How would you start a conversation with her? Think of a few things you would tell her about your semester and one question to ask her to keep the conversation going.

IV Reading

A. Read the letter that a group of Chinese exchange students wrote to their American classmates, then mark the statements that follow true (T) or false (F).

下个星期学校要开始放假了。我们要回中国了。这个学期我们在美国很快乐，因为我们认识了很多新朋友，还加入了很多很酷的俱乐部。虽然我们要回中国了，但是我们希望还能经常和你们打电话。最后，祝你们的中文成绩越来越好！

	T	F
1. The new semester starts next week.	○	○
2. The exchange students will return to China over school vacation.	○	○
3. The exchange students have made lots of new friends and joined many cool clubs while studying in America.	○	○
4. Because they are returning to China, they don't plan to keep in touch with their American classmates.	○	○
5. They hope their American classmates' Chinese grades will get better and better.	○	○

B. Read the passage then mark the statements that follow true (T) or false (F).

虽然我这个学期的中文成绩已经很好了，但是我希望下个学期的成绩可以更好，所以我放假的时候想去北京学中文。我希望在那儿能认识些新朋友，多说中文。下个学期回美国的时候，我的中文一定比现在更好。

	T	F
1. The writer says that his Chinese grades are already very good this semester.	○	○
2. The writer says he hopes to practice his Chinese pronunciation over the break.	○	○
3. The writer says that next semester, his Chinese will definitely be better than it is now.	○	○

A. Use the words in the list to complete the passage. Use each word only once.

Choices: 新，学期，放假，成绩，虽然，回，但是

今天我的心情很好，因为我知道了这个 ＿＿＿＿＿＿＿ 的数学 ＿＿＿＿＿＿＿。＿＿＿＿＿＿＿ 这个学期的数学课比以前的数学课难，＿＿＿＿＿＿＿ 我这个学期的成绩比以前的成绩好。我得谢谢我的 ＿＿＿＿＿＿＿ 朋友。她数学学得很好，她经常帮我复习和预习。明天我们学校要开始 ＿＿＿＿＿＿＿ 了。我希望下个学期 ＿＿＿＿＿＿＿ 学校的时候，我还能和她一起学习

B. What do you think this girl is hoping for? Write her thoughts on the lines below.

＿＿＿＿＿＿＿＿＿＿＿＿＿＿＿＿＿＿＿＿＿＿＿＿＿＿＿

＿＿＿＿＿＿＿＿＿＿＿＿＿＿＿＿＿＿＿＿＿＿＿＿＿＿＿

＿＿＿＿＿＿＿＿＿＿＿＿＿＿＿＿＿＿＿＿＿＿＿＿＿＿＿

＿＿＿＿＿＿＿＿＿＿＿＿＿＿＿＿＿＿＿＿＿＿＿＿＿＿＿

Put the Pieces Together!

I Chapter Vocabulary Chart

Fill in the pinyin for and the definition of each word that you learned in this chapter. Use the extra spaces at the end of the chart to add any additional words you have learned.

No.	Word	Pinyin	Definition
1	加入		
2	俱乐部		
3	认识		
4	新		
5	得		
6	最近		
7	唱歌		
8	跳舞		
9	应该		
10	聊天儿		
11	玩儿		

No.	Word	Pinyin	Definition
12	见面		
13	酷		
14	放假		
15	回		
16	学期		
17	虽然		
18	希望		
19	成绩		

II Reading

A. It's the end of the semester and two students, Tiantian and Wenwen, have written a thank you card to their Chinese teacher. Read the card and mark the statements that follow true (T) or false (F).

白老师，你好！

　　谢谢你这个学期教我们中文！虽然有的时候中文课的作业有点儿多，但是我们都觉得中文学起来很有意思。我们最近加入了中文俱乐部，认识了些新朋友。我们和他们一起玩儿，聊天儿，还一起唱中文歌，跳中国舞。这个俱乐部太酷了！我们明天要放假了。你说过你会回北京。我们也会去北京玩儿。我们希望能跟你在北京见面！

天天，文文

	T	F
1. Tiantian and Wenwen say that they always have too much Chinese homework.	○	○
2. Tiantian and Wenwen joined the Chinese club.	○	○
3. Tiantian and Wenwen can chat, sing Chinese songs, and dance at Chinese Club.	○	○
4. Mr. Bai will stay in the United States during school vacation.	○	○
5. Tiantian and Wenwen hope to meet up with Mr. Bai in Beijing.	○	○

III Writing

A. Imagine that you attend Martin and Isabella's school, and you would like to start a new club. First, you have to fill out the form below to tell the principal more about your proposed club.

1. 你们俱乐部的名字是什么？

_____

2. 你们俱乐部星期几见面？ 你们几点见面？

_____

3. 你计划跟朋友们在俱乐部做什么？

_____

_____